English Map-Making 1500–1650
Historical Essays

English Map-Making
1500~1650

Historical essays edited by Sarah Tyacke

The British Library

© 1983 The British Library Board

Published by the British Library, Reference Division Publications
Great Russell Street, London WC1B 3DG

BRITISH LIBRARY CATALOGUING IN PUBLICATION DATA

   Tyacke, Sarah
     English map-making 1500–1650
     1. Cartography—England—History
     I. Title
     526'.0942   GA231

ISBN 0 7123 0010 4

Designed by Alan Bartram
Phototypeset in Palatino 10/13 by Tradespools Ltd. Frome, Somerset.
Printed in Great Britain at The Moxon Press, Ilkley.

Contents

List of illustrations

Acknowledgements

The editor would like to thank the following people for their assistance in the preparation of this volume, John Simmons, Christopher Woolgar, P.I. King, F.C. Jolly, Robin Harcourt-Williams, Peter Barber, Gillian Hill, Elizabeth Clutton, Tony Campbell, Dr Helen Wallis and my colleagues in the Map Library and BL Photographic Service. Further acknowledgements relating to specific chapters are given by the individual contributors at the end of each essay and in the list of illustrations. The index was prepared by Gillian Hill.

ABBREVIATIONS

BL   British Library
CSP   *Calendar of State Papers*
PRO   Public Record Office
DNB   *Dictionary of National Biography*

List of contributors

J.H. Andrews
Professor of Geography, Trinity College, Dublin. His publications include *A Paper Landscape: The Ordnance Survey in the Nineteenth Century* (1975) and articles in *Imago Mundi, Proceedings of the Royal Irish Academy etc.*

Peter Eden
Formerely Senior Lecturer in English Topography, Leicester University. His publications include *Dictionary of Land Surveyors and Local Cartographers of Great Britain, 1550–1850 and Ireland* (1979).

J.B. Harley
Montefiore Reader in Geography in the University of Exeter. He has written extensively on the history of English map-making and is currently co-editor of the forthcoming general *History of Cartography* to be published by the University of Chicago Press.

Marcus Merriman
Lecturer at the University of Lancaster and a student of Scottish-French-English relations during the minority of Mary Queen of Scots. He contributed the northern borders section in Volume IV of *The History of the King's Works.*

Victor Morgan
Lecturer in history at the University of East Anglia, Norwich. His research interests include the history of the universities and the idea of the country in English politics and society.

William Ravenhill
Reardon Smith professor of Geography, University of Exeter. His publications include *Benjamin Donn's map of Devon* (1965), *John Norden's manuscript maps of Cornwall* (1972) and articles in *Imago Mundi, Cartographic Journal etc.*

John Roche
Teacher of the history of the exact sciences at Linacre College, Oxford. His research interests include the history of astronomy and navigation in the Renaissance, and the foundation period of electromagnetism.

John Schofield
Field Officer in charge of current excavations in the city of London for the Museum of London. He was the principal editor of *Archaeology of the City of London* (1980), and *Recent Archaeological Research in English Towns* (1981). At present he is working on *The Building of London: from the Conquest to the Great Fire* to be published in 1983.

G.L'E. Turner
Senior Assistant Curator, Museum of the History of Science, University of Oxford. His publications include *Antique Scientific Instruments* (1980), *Essays on the History of the Microscope* (1980). He is currently editor of *Annals of Science.*

Sarah Tyacke

Introduction

Earlier versions of the essays published here were first presented at a British Library seminar held at the Reference Division on 13 March 1981. They represent some of the varying aspects of current research into the history of map-making in Britain for the period 1500–1650. Three distinct, but related themes were considered: the meaning and function of maps in this period, the developments in methods of survey and in drawing maps in the sixteenth century, and the emergence of a number of surveyors who began to draw maps as part of their normal duties.

It has perhaps become a commonplace, if a controversial one, in the historical study of maps that the discipline is ill-defined and has often been subsumed in other related areas of intellectual thought, notably geography, the history of discoveries, historical geography, and scientific, military, architectural, and other forms of history.[1] Some have gone so far as to claim that there is no such subject and that what passes for cartographic history is an antiquarian interest in maps as artefacts: an interest normally associated with collectors.[2] These somewhat pessimistic and critical views, however, do make explicit an awareness which has long been implicit,[3] that the history of cartography should be a discrete subject and one which is able to make a contribution to a wide range of historical studies as well as being concerned with the recording and cataloguing of maps. Against this background the present volume attempts to provide new information about various aspects of maps and map-making and related subjects and to offer some views on the interpretation of map history for the period 1500–1650, when maps were first drawn and used on a wide scale.

The contributors are from a number of different academic backgrounds, reflecting the fact that the history of cartography is not the preserve of any one group and reflecting also the natural association of map history with other subjects. Among the contributors and participants at the seminar were a mediæval historian, a military historian, historians of science, geographers, local historians, museum curators, librarians, archivists, collectors and academics. Not only is the diversity of their interests and their methods of approach revealed in the present volume, but so is the extent to which students in different but related fields can contribute to one another's studies – in this case the history of map making in Britain.

The first two essays, *Meaning and ambiguity in Tudor cartography* and *The literary image of globes and maps in early modern England*, address themselves to the question of how to describe and interpret the layers of meaning present in a map and what such symbolic meanings might have meant to those who made maps, saw them, or used them in this period. The authors argue, from their different standpoints, that an appreciation of the context in which maps were drawn and used is necessary before the history of maps can be written. This type of approach goes beyond considering the practical function of maps and can encompass discussion of, for example, map content from a social or intellectual viewpoint. Only occasionally in this period, however, are the intentions of the map maker made plain by a written text: in the case of Samuel Walker's map of the manor of Garnetts in Essex, 1622,[4] (pl. 4) his title explains that he has, by design and presumably for the lord of the manor Sir William Fitch, included comprehensive information about 'everie gatehouse, barnes, stables . . . orchards, yardes, gardens, highwaies . . . gates . . . fielde, woods, springs [etc] . . . , and the chappell, mansion house, and other ten[emen]ts in their true places and order'.

The next essay directs itself to a particular problem in the history of the period. In *Italian military engineers in Britain in the 1540s* Marcus Merriman describes the context in which the transmission of surveying and drawing skills to English military surveyors was probably made: in particular the way in which the use of plans drawn to scale emerged at the same time as the introduction of *trace italienne* fortifications in the English territories in France, and English coastal and Anglo-Scottish border areas in the 1540s. This theme was developed by Paul Harvey in his seminar paper on the introduction of drawn scales on local maps and plans with particular reference to a 1545 manuscript map of Portsmouth. A version of this paper was subsequently published in *Hampshire Studies*.[5]

The volume also reflects a growing interest amongst historians in the estate surveyors who began to draw maps in this period and more especially in their emergence as an identifiable group. Peter Eden, whose index of land surveyors of Great Britain and Ireland 1550–1850 continues to grow, has compiled the professional biographies of three sixteenth-century surveyors, beginning with Peter Kempe, (employed by Sir William Cecil *c.* 1560–1576/7), and continuing with his servant Thomas Clerke and his servant Thomas Langdon. From such multiple biographies emerges the nature and development of estate mapping and its relationship to legal and agrarian change. They also reveal the personal and professional mechanisms through which the surveyors' skills were diffused and the appreciation by landowners of such skills. Thomas Langdon, for example, was an MA of New College, Oxford, had studied civil law and eventually became a country parson. His patrons included a number of Oxford colleges and the Gresham family. Similarly, from the listing of surveyors for the sixteenth century in Peter Eden's *Dictionary*[6] one finds that the estate surveyors who drew maps were also schoolmasters, instrument-makers, mathematical practitioners, masons, manorial stewards and engineers. By contrast John Andrews commented on the paucity of Irish estate mapping before the 1580s and pointed out that only with the Munster plantation of 1586 were four surveyors brought in to measure and map the confiscated portions of the counties of Waterford, Cork, Limerick and Kerry.[7] The theme of the surveying profession was concluded by a study of Ralph Treswell the elder (b 1566, d 1616), not in his more usual guise as a surveyor of estates both rural and urban, but as a drawer of building plans for London landlords. John Schofield makes it clear that this specialised form of plan drawing was required to distinguish between different landlords' tenements in the same building at a time when the population of London was pressing hard upon the available dwelling space.

As the drawing and use of maps and plans began to be integrated into everyday life, so to speak, the allied crafts of measuring, arithmetic, geometry, surveying and instrument-making were also developing and influencing map making, drawing and production. Gerard Turner, John Roche and (with particular reference to Christopher Saxton) William Ravenhill consider various aspects of the interaction of those scientific skills with map-making. Clear unequivocal evidence for the use of particular types of instrument or indeed of any instruments at all in surveying is hard to come by. From literary evidence, for example, the cross-staff seems to have been used, but some of the more innovative variations of cross-staffs which were proposed by contemporaries should, as John Roche notes, be viewed with scepticism.[8] From the evidence of surveying accounts, correspondence, and the maps themselves little has so far been gleaned on the type of instruments and surveying done. In this respect the manuscript map or chart of Milford Haven drawn by George Owen of Henllys in 1596 (pl. 2) and included in his *Description of Pembroke* apparently dedicated to his kinsman Henry, second Earl of Pembroke, is significant. The map is now known only from a copy made by John Thornton in 1687 for Samuel Pepys[9] and bound with a manuscript of the *Description of Pembroke* which Pepys notes in his catalogue as being 'Ld Burghley's Book'. George Owen records in his *Description* how he made the survey by indirect means and, in the legend on the map itself, made it clear that the distances, scale and places in the map were 'all don by Instrument', which as he pointedly remarked of the distances between Rat Iland, the Stack and Dale Poynt could not be done otherwise – as they were either islands or coastal features.[10] Peter Eden notes the use and costs of using a chain in estate surveying[11] and makes the point that the surveyor seems to have normally provided his own instruments, requiring from his employers the provision of parchment, oils, ink, and colours, and some local assistance. John Roche records the use of the cross-staff by Sir William Lower[12] in measuring lands in 1607. Similarly William Ravenhill ingeniously proposes that Christopher Saxton made use of the beacon system in England and Wales to view and map the country by some form of triangulation. The technical infrastructure necessary for such activities was provided by such instrument-makers as Humphrey Cole, whose work Gerard Turner examines.[13] In particular he describes an alidade of 1582 by Cole which seems to be the only English plane-table alidade surviving; its use was described by Thomas Digges in his *Pantometria* of 1591.

This selection of essays cannot cover all aspects of map-making in Britain in this period, neither do any of the contributions attempt a comparison with the continent, nor with earlier periods. In terms of numbers of maps, before 1500 approximately thirty local maps are preserved but in the period 1500–1550 between 150 and 200 are known.[14] This rapid and dramatic rise in numbers seems to have been the result not merely of a better rate of survival but also, as remarked above, of the increasing use of maps for a number of different purposes; these were normally drawn to a given scale and oriented with some degree of precision. The problem of how such scale-drawing skills were introduced, as discussed by Marcus Merriman and Paul Harvey, invites further discussion on related subjects: for example, the relatively new use of orientation, of conventional symbols, and of perspective. As the methods of drawing and giving scales to maps and plans are investigated, so for example the orientation symbols and thought processes behind them require further consideration, as E.G.R. Taylor noted some thirty years ago, in her article *The South-pointing Needle*.[15] In William Cuningham's picture of the horizontal surveying instrument[16] in *The*

Cosmographical Glasse the needle on the compass used for direction finding and survey is south-pointing. The use of such instruments seems to have had a direct relationship to map-making – William Smith's plan of Bristol of 1568[17] is oriented with south at the top and expresses this orientation by a compass circle and south-pointing needle in the manner of the Nuremberg compass-dial makers of the period.

In order to appreciate the widespread alteration in attitudes to topography and mapping in this period some comparison with those of earlier periods seems essential.[18] The earliest surviving maps of Great Britain date from the mid-thirteenth century; the earliest local plans, associated with a variety of functions, – manorial, property boundaries, location of water courses etc – date from the end of the twelfth century. These pictorial or diagrammatic maps seem however to have been drawn in isolation; they did not become widespread nor fashionable. In the fifteenth century this still seems true. In her article on antiquarian studies in fifteenth century England,[19] Antonia Gransden places particular emphasis on two fifteenth century topographically-minded antiquaries, Thomas Elmham and Thomas Burton. Elmsham, in his history of St Augustine's monastery at Canterbury dating from the early fifteenth century, uses a plan of the island of Thanet to illustrate the legend of Dompneva's hind. King Edgar promised to give St Augustine's the area delineated by the course of the hind running across the island of Thanet.[20] Elmham explains in the text that the route taken by the hind is shown by a green line while the red lines show the roads from one parish to another. The idea of illustrating a story by such a plan does not seem to have been copied widely; nor was the use of similarly devised maps and plans for other purposes at all usual. Written itineraries, written accounts of estates, and written topographies seem to have been considered sufficient, although on occasion, as in the case of Hardyng's Chronicle, a diagrammatic map was again used to illustrate the text – 'A carte and figure of Scotlande' dated to 1457[21]. In a sense this limited appreciation and use of mapping is hardly surprising as the detailed topographic information which can be imparted by a text can never be expressed in its entirety on a map; not until maps could be made approximating to a required level of information could they provide more than a very generalised *aide-memoire*.

In the middle decades of the sixteenth century however the situation seems to have changed, picture maps were used increasingly by statesmen, landowners, military engineers[22] and others. References to the making of maps begin to increase. In 1538, for example, Sir Richard Gresham, Lord Mayor of London, sent Thomas Cromwell, Lord Privy Seal, plans for a Bourse in London. He remarked in his letter – 'last yere I shewyd your goode lordeshipe a platte, that was drawn howte for to make a goodly Burse in Lombert Strette for Marchaunts to repayer unto'.[23] Similarly in pursuance of his act abolishing sanctuaries except for parish churches, yards, cathedrals and hospitals Henry VIII issued a commission to the Mayor of Norwich and others, requiring them to make a map on parchment[24] and to set out therein the bounds and limits of the city as a sanctuary. In 1541 according to the accounts of the chamberlains of the City of Norwich 'vjs viid was p^d to Boswell for correctynge the platte for the sayntwarye [sanctuary].' The commission dated 1541 and a certificate are attached to the map. The latter, signed by the Mayor and others, claimed that they had personally gone to the city and 'viewed it and every part thereof'.

As earlier, maps were on occasion used in legal cases – the diagrammatic map of Pleyden, Iden and Brookland (pl. 3) was found amongst the depositions of the prior of Christchurch, Canterbury, and used in his case against Thomas Cheney in 1537[25]. The case concerned the title to 28 acres of marshland called Scottsmarshe lying in the Walland marsh on the borders of Kent and Sussex which both the prior of Christchurch and Sir Thomas Cheney claimed. The documents accompanying the map include both the questions to be put to the various deponents and their answers. One of the deponents, Sir Giles Alyngton, was to be asked, on the prior's behalf, whether he knew the Scottsmarshe, 'if he had seyn [seen] a plotte of the . . . messuage', and also if 'the meeres and bounds of the said pa[rc]el or messuage called Scottsmarshe be expressed in the same evydence . . . and in whose kepynge the same evidence was, when the same plotte should be made and by whom and to what intent'. Sir Giles in response to these questions said that he had seen the land in question but did not know 'how it boundeth'. He did however produce the map which he apparently then copied for his examiners. He said that the 'plat conteyning the pariss[h]es' had come into his possession about twelve years past and had been made for an earlier dispute over the same marshland between Thomas Elyngton and Sir Thomas Cheney. If the map itself is compared with a later one showing the Walland and Denge marshes drawn about 1592 for All Souls College Oxford (pl. 5) the area shown becomes reasonably apparent.[26] At the top of the diagrammatic map is what was called the Appledore channel passing between Rye and Guildford; to the right the Kyte marsh partly belonging to the prior of Christchurch, at the left 'Abbates marshe', at the bottom the road presumably running past Fairfield. Both the bridges and the gate seem to have been drawn with some precision. Within the boundaries of the marshland shown, land belonging to the parishes of Brookland, Iden, Pleyden and Brenzett is indicated. The exact relationship between the court case and this diagrammatic map is unclear but the appreciation by the prior of Christchurch of a map's potential worth in a legal dispute is obvious – especially as in this case when the area under dispute was not readily identifiable by the deponents. This copy of the map was drawn by the local landowner Sir Giles Alyngton from the earlier one in his possession. It incorporated prominent local features as a means of identifying the generalised location of the ownership of land in the area. It does not identify the disputed land, merely the locality; the witnesses gave oral evidence of a much more detailed kind on the boundaries involved.

The use of maps in legal disputes seems to have been more common on the continent where, as in France and the Low Countries, local pictorial and diagrammatic map making by painters had a longer tradition, apparently as a result of various boundary and other disputes;[27] in the case of southern France the maps and plans preserved in notarial archives were drawn from the 1420s.[28] In the Low Countries similar examples may be found. A particularly fine example of such a pictorial map-view is to be found in the Royal Archives in Brussels – a panorama of the river Scheldt and environs from Rupelmonde to the island of Walcheren dated to 1468[29] (pl. 1). The map follows the course of the river and its northern tributaries as if viewed from the south. On the section covering the lower Scheldt there are overlays of parchment showing houses. This map-view has been associated by Gottschalk and Unger[30] with various disputes over water tolls on the river in the late fifteenth century.

The phenomenon of the legal map was evidently one way in which mapping became more widespread. At the same time particular types of mapping for special purposes were also increasing. For the period 1550–1600 Eden records at least twenty surveyors who made maps other than estate or manorial ones; these could be, as Marcus Merriman and John Schofield show, military or urban plans, as well as, for example, boundary, harbour, and drainage maps. In the case of the *Description of North Walland, South Walland and Dengemarshe* the evident purpose was to represent local drainage patterns (pl. 5). The legend notes that the plott described 'the common watercourses with theire heades armes pinnockes bridges and principall guttes.' As at a later date, notes indicating types of land use were also often included on general maps and on occasion the landowner added his own remarks. William Cecil indicated on one of his estate maps (pl. 31) those fields which grew corn. More interestingly for the history of cartography, it was apparently Cecil who, in order to evaluate in some way the lead and copper mines in the country, drew, or had drawn, a 'thematic' map[31] showing the distribution of such mines in south-west England and Wales. The mines, labelled 'cuperum' and 'plumbum' were distinguished by a cross and located on a very simplified outline map.[32]

The increasing use and appreciation of maps of whatever sort amongst the educated and landowning sections of society seems to have occurred within the space of sixty years, from about the 1530s to the 1590s. The extent to which the attendant skills of map making had also been acquired and were being utilised can be visually measured by comparing the diagrammatic map of the Walland marsh in 1537 (pl. 3) and the same area drawn by a professional surveyor employed by All Souls College about 1592 (pl. 5). Not that there was an overall or steady improvement in map-making skills. The traditional diagrammatic or pictorial map continued to be used until the end of the century. The change was that maps, diagrammatic or pictorial, measured on the ground or sketched from memory, imagined or used as literary or social metaphors, had become an integral part of ways of thinking about the country.

1. M.J. Blakemore and J.B. Harley 'Concepts in the History of Cartography' *Cartographica*, 17, no. 4, monograph 26 (1980), p. 1.

2. D. Wood: Review of P.D.A. Harvey The History of topographical maps: symbols, pictures and surveys. London, 1980. In: *Cartographica* 17, no. 3 (Autumn 1980).

3. *Imago Mundi* the earliest journal to be devoted solely to the history of cartography, was first published in 1935.

4. A map of the manor of Garnetts, Essex owned by Sir William Fitch and drawn by Samuel Walker 1622. BL Add. MS 41848. I am indebted to my colleague Peter Barber for drawing my attention to this map.

5. See P.D.A. Harvey: 'The Portsmouth map of 1545 and the Introduction of Scale Maps into England' in *Hampshire Studies* presented to Dorothy Dymond. (Portsmouth, 1981), pp. 33–49.

6. P. Eden, *Dictionary of land surveyors and local cartographers of Great Britain and Ireland 1550–1850* (Folkestone, 1979).

7. See below pp. 20–1 for an abstract of John Andrew's paper given at the seminar on 13 March 1981.

8. See below p. 109.

9. Magdalene College, Cambridge, Pepys MS 1296. A note in Pepys's hand records that the original was 'torne out' and that it was 'remayneing in ye hands of the present Earle of Carbery', *ie* Richard Vaughan second Earl of Carbery. He goes on to record that the 'original above mention'd was presented to his Mts [*ie* Majesty] . . . by ye Earle of Carbery the 15 November 1687'. At Hatfield House there is a map of Milford Haven, undated, (CPM II.15) and there is another version at BL Cotton MS Aug. I.ii.20, also undated. Both have been dated by R.A. Skelton to the mid-1590s but evidently neither is the original from which this copy by Thornton was made.

10. B.G. Charles, *George Owen of Henllys: a Welsh Elizabethan* (Aberystwyth, 1973), pp. 65–6, 154–5.

11. See below pp. 73–4.

12. See below p. 110.

13. See below pp. 100–1.

14. *Local Maps and plans from medieval England*, edited by P.D.A. Harvey and R.A. Skelton, (Oxford, forthcoming) introduction and chapter 4.

15. E.G.R. Taylor, 'The South-pointing Needle'. *Imago Mundi*, 8 (1951), 1–7.

16. W. Cuningham, *The Cosmographical Glasse*, (London, 1559), p. 136.

17. *William Smith, The Particular Description of England 1588*, edited by H.B. Wheatley (1879), pl. xxv.

18. See below p. 26 where John Hale's vivid description is quoted of the limited appreciation of topography in medieval Europe even when the position of boundaries were, so to speak, at stake.

19. A. Gransden, 'Antiquarian studies in fifteenth century England' *Antiquarian Journal*, 60 (1980), 75–97.

20. *Historia Monasterii S. Augustini Cantuariensis*, edited by Charles Hardwick, Rolls Series (London, 1858). The frontispiece is a reproduction of the map of Thanet. See also P.D.A. Harvey and R.A. Skelton, *Local Maps* (forthcoming) for a reproduction of the original at Trinity Hall (MS 1.f.63) and a full discussion.

21. D.G. Moir, *The early maps of Scotland* (Edinburgh, 1973), p.6. The manuscript map in Hardying's Chronicle dated to 1457 is at BL Lansdowne MS 204. ff.226v and 227.

22. See pl. 20 A map of Castlemilk in Dumfriesshire made by Thomas Petyt *c*1547 for presentation to the Duke of Somerset.

23. Quoted in 'George Monoux, the Man and his Work' in *Walthamstow Antiquarian Society,* 17 (1927), p. 12. See also E. Lynam, 'English Maps and Map Makers of the Sixteenth Century', *Geographical Journal* 116 (1950), p. 7, and Add MS18783, 'The Leiger Book of the estates of George Monoux of Walthamstow', in which is drawn a plan of St John's Fields at Chapel End (f.81) and which is dated to *c*1528. The property was granted to the Monoux family by the Prior of the Hospital of St John of Jerusalem in 1528.

24. The map (PRO MPI 221) is described by W.T. Bentley in *The Streets and lanes of the city of Norwich*, edited by J. Kirkpatrick (1889). The certificate is translated on p. 117 (Act 32 Henry VIII c.12).

25. PRO MPA 61 and C.24/3 No. 12. For another example of a map made apparently for some sort of dispute over watercourses, which has recently come to light, see 'Plan of Watercourses and mill at East Heslerton, Yorkshire' – dated to the first half of the sixteenth century. BL Department of Manuscripts Deposit 7592 fol. 167r.

26. All Souls College, Oxford, Hovenden map MS.III.14. North and South Walland marshes, pl. 5.

27. See C. Koeman 'Die Darstellungsmethoden von Bauten auf alten Karten' in *Wolfenbütteler Forschungen*, 7 (1980), 147–193.

28. F. Dainville 'Cartes et contestations au XVe siècle' in *Imago Mundi* 24 (1970), 87–94. A few comparably early examples from England are to be found in the Duchy of Lancaster records in the Public Record Office.

29. *Inventaire des cartes et plans, manuscrits et gravés, qui sont conservés aux Archives Générales du Royaume.* (Bruxelles, 1848), p. 46, no. 351. Section of the map (521 cm long) showing the town of Antwerp and the opposite bank viewed from the south.

30. See M.K.E. Gottschalk and W.S. Unger, 'De Oudste Kaarten der Waterwegen tussen Brabant, Vlaanderen en Zeeland', *Tijdschrift van het Koninklijk Netherlands Aardrijkskundig Genootschap* 67, (1950), 146–159. For other maps of this period see Y.M. Donkersloot-de Vrij, *Topografische Kaarten van Nederland voor 1750* (Groningen, 1981).

31. Map of south-west England and south Wales showing locations of lead and copper mines, possibly drawn by Sir William Cecil *c*1570. (Hatfield House, CPM supp. 1).

32. Cf. Arthur H. Robinson, *Early Thematic Mapping in the History of Cartography* (Chicago, 1982), p.x, where he says that 'the idea . . . of showing the geographical structure of one phenomenon seems not have occurred to anyone' before the second half of the seventeenth century. This does not seem to be the case. The idea of such a map obviously occurred to Cecil and no doubt to others, although their capacity to express such ideas cartographically was limited.

J.H. Andrews

Appendix: the beginnings of the surveying profession in Ireland – abstract

'We had more ado with Ireland than all the world besides', remarked James I after inspecting the contents of his state paper office. Irish map history is very badly served by sixteenth-century printed books, family and estate papers, and local-government records, but the collection that impressed King James does include some interesting references to surveying and surveyors.

Paradoxically, extant maps are not a major source of evidence in this connection. There are many large-scale Tudor representations of Irish battles, forts, and walled towns; and many contemporary small-scale Irish topographical surveys in the manner of Saxton or Pont. But these maps were mainly produced by English military engineers on short visits, and such transients can hardly be said to constitute an Irish surveying profession; there was certainly nothing distinctively Irish about either their methods or their style.

Another and more promising field of inquiry concerns the forfeitures and redistributions of landed property that followed many of Ireland's numerous wars and rebellions. Four such episodes claim special attention: (a) surveys of scattered monastic lands following the dissolution of 1536–9; (b) the attempted English colonisation of the midland territories of Leix and Offaly in and after 1556; (c) the 'composition' of Connaught in 1585, a territorial inventory which was unusual in not being accompanied by a programme of colonisation; (d) the Munster plantation of 1586–9, famous for its associations with Walter Raleigh and Edmund Spenser.

All four operations involved the assignment of both areal and monetary values to numerous small parcels of land, but for the first three there appear to be no unambiguous references to specialist land surveyors and most of the associated acreage figures are too 'round' to be anything but estimates or guesses. It was only with the Munster plantation that English colonists began to require an exact admeasurement of their estates, and in 1586 four surveyors were brought in to measure and map the newly confiscated portions of Counties Waterford, Cork, Limerick and Kerry. These men – Arthur Robins, Francis Jobson, John Lawson and Richard Whittaker – are the first identifiable 'estate surveyors' in Irish history and there are some sparse but noteworthy records of their earnings, their surveying techniques, and their conditions of work; there are also two maps (both in the National Maritime Museum, Greenwich) which may give some impression of their cartographic style.

After the official Munster survey some of the new landowners wrote of employing private surveyors to subdivide their estates into tenant farms. One such tenement map survives: it dates from 1598 and shows Sir Walter Raleigh's property at Mogeely, Co. Cork. This map has often been attributed to John White (better known for his map of Virginia), but the only Anglo-Irish land surveyor positively known to have remained at work in the middle or late 1590s is Francis Jobson, who was offered employment by several of the Munster planters and who also made maps for at least two landowners in other parts of the country. It seems however that there were not yet enough private openings in Ireland to support a full-time practitioner, and Jobson is also found accepting dangerous and ill-paid military commissions for which he probably had little relish.

Jobson's name makes another appearance in 1615, in a record of official surveyors employed on the plantation of Co. Longford. By that time (if it was the same Jobson) he might claim to be the father of the Irish surveying profession. By that time, too, the recent history of Ireland had repeated itself. The Earl of Tyrone's rebellion of 1598–1603 had brought a new generation of engineers and map-makers into Ireland, some of whom stayed to work on a new series of plantation surveys in Ulster and elsewhere, and at least one of whom (Thomas Raven) was later to flourish as a private estate surveyor. From Raven onwards an Irish surveying tradition has continued unbroken until recent times, but in the present state of knowledge it is difficult to distinguish the cartographic legacy of the 1600s from that of the 1580s.

J.B. Harley

Meaning and ambiguity
in Tudor cartography

Elizabeth, great empress of the world,
Britannia's Atlas, star of England's globe,
That sways the massy sceptre of her land,
And holds the royal reins of Albion...[1]

This essay is concerned with the meaning – in the broadest sense of the word – of Tudor maps and plans. It contends that to contemporaries in the sixteenth and seventeenth centuries maps often meant more than a geographical representation of the features of a country, a county, a town or a local rural estate. In many contexts maps would have articulated symbolic values as part of a visual language by which specific interests, doctrines, and even world views were communicated. Maps were one of a number of instruments of control by landlords and governments; they were spatial emblems of power in society; they were artefacts in the creation of myth; and they influenced perceptions of place and space at a variety of geographical scales. Accordingly they can be considered to form part of intellectual history rather than standing as documents apart from the development of thought in early modern England. Yet the substantive literature on the history of Tudor cartography has been primarily concerned with biography, with carto-bibliography and with the beginnings of an English map trade, with technical questions relating to the construction of maps and the tools and techniques employed, with the transmission of such techniques from continental Europe, and, amongst historians in particular, with the maps as topographical and geographical records.[2] Such approaches are all reflected in this volume, but this paper aims to supplement them in the twilight zone of what might be called 'cartographic semantics'. This is a gap in understanding the historicity of Tudor cartography,[3] but at the same time the paper provides an opportunity to make a more general statement about cartographic meaning and the potential of a method of iconographical analysis through which it may be uncovered.

Few would deny that the history of cartography ought to concern itself with the study of map images[4] and their formation, transmission, and transformation in various cultures and time periods. Cartographic semantics may accordingly be defined as the branch of the history of cartography which is concerned with the meaning of map images. In this paper the subject matter will be restricted to a consideration of the meanings which contemporaries may have ascribed to particular maps in the period of early modern England when they were first created. Once created, map images, like images in art in general, acquired an independent life and survived beyond the society into which they were born. With regard to English county maps, for example, Saxton's surveys provided in the late sixteenth century a series of 'archetype' maps and 'archetypal meanings', but it has to be recognised that the meanings originally attached to these images were subject to change. Saxton's county maps were reinterpreted by successive generations of cartographers in the light of their own perceptions and preoccupations, so by the second half of the eighteenth century it is likely that the last states of this Tudor atlas[5] were expected to evoke a largely antiquarian image, rather then reflecting Elizabethan notions of landscape and territory. They would have found their market – and social impact – in a print industry that was by then catering for Romantic taste.

Even when the exercise becomes historically specific, the identification of meaning according to acceptable rules of evidence is not an easy matter. The basic question, 'What did map x mean to beholder y' is never in fact straightforward. As E.H. Gombrich has observed of images in general, they

apparently occupy a curious position somewhere between the statements of language, which are intended to convey a meaning, and the things of nature, to which we only can give a meaning.[6]

It could be added that the position of the map is even more curious. Many of the maps of Tudor and early Stuart England depended on written captions – to say nothing of place-names – for part of the meaning to be triggered in the minds of their users. They present an intractable problem of duality. In several respects – such as those of written language and graphic image, of mimetic and abstract sign, of art and science, and of reality and deliberate idealisation – the map image is a hybrid. The literature has recognised some of these seemingly antipathetical qualities[7], but how can we begin to untie the Gordian knot posed by semantic enquiry?

Meaning: an iconographical approach

Neither one deft blow of a single methodological strategy nor a handy parcel of documents tumbling from a standard archival source is likely to resolve the conundrums of meaning which attach to various types of Tudor maps. Cartographic semantics are still largely at the stage of being a theoretical problem and there are few studies which will illustrate directly how meaning might be dissected or, indeed, which will effectively identify the characteristics of meaning for which we are supposed to be searching. As a result, this paper, although it aims to keep in touch with historical reality be selecting examples which appear to elucidate the concepts under discussion, is inevitably more hypothetical than empirical in nature, and some of its statements remain unsupported. This problem is itself a striking illustration of the need for the history of cartography to adopt a more interdisciplinary approach. Many subjects – including architecture, art history, archaeology, historical geography, literature, and social anthropology – have all long ago embarked on a search for meaning in the buildings, images, artefacts, landscapes, myths, rituals and writings of the societies they study. Nor is this a similarity only of semantic objective because these disciplines have all drawn on a related methodology, sometimes identified as a communication model and in other contexts as a semiotic approach.[8] The iconographical approach[9] has been traditionally associated with art history and with the 'art as communication' paradigm, but in this paper it will be argued that it offers some particularly apposite directions for a study of meaning in the history of cartography. It has already been advocated as such a potential strategy to assist in the descriptive and classificatory study of cartographic images with the aim of understanding the direct or indirect meaning of the subject matter represented.[10] That it has proved its value in the study of images may be judged from the substantial literature it has generated from the nineteenth century onwards, to the extent that it may be regarded as the most general and all-embracing method for the historical interpretation of art. The development of a new critical strategy in the last half century has owed much to the formulations of the late Erwin Panofsky, especially in his *Studies in Iconology* (1939)[11]. The methodological principles set out in that book have, it is suggested, a direct application to the interpretation of cartographic images.

For Panofsky, iconography was 'that branch of the history of art which concerns itself with the subject matter or meaning of works of art, as opposed to their form'[12]. Thus, he was postulating three levels of meaning in painting and other art forms – which were also stages of interpretation – and while an exact transfer of his terminology to the history of cartography would be inappropriate, its basic strategy, involving a search for deeper meaning in the image, is arguably highly relevant. Despite the intermingling of graphic and written languages in cartography, we are still dealing with the meaning of images in a sense analogous to the history of art. The barrier is that historians of cartography, whose studies have been focused on the technical improvements of maps, have tended to over-emphasise the differences between pictures and maps even suggesting that in the Renaissance what is seen as a split between cartography and art was finally accomplished through the introduction of more technically perfect methods of surveying and map drawing.[13] It is asserted here, however, that despite the undoubted technical improvements in Tudor cartography, which involved the new systems of instrumentation and indirect measurement described elsewhere in this volume, maps still retained some of the crucial communicative properties of pictures. Maps do not become, by dint of geometry and rational scales alone, a different class of image and, in the identification of meaning, it may be better to regard them as a specialised type of 'geometrical picture', in which geometry was part of the message, rather than not as pictures at all.[14]

If this premise – that cartographic images are quintessentially similar to the images viewed in architecture, painting or sculpture – is accepted then it is possible, without unduly distorting the intention of the scheme, to match Panofsky's three levels of meaning with three analogous levels in the image presented by the map. The three parrallels in the two types of image, in art and cartography, are set out opposite (Table 1), and the text which follows exemplifies the implications of such a division of meanings. Panofsky's terminology is sometimes at cross purposes with cartographic usage and it is suggested that we ought to accept the broad *intent* of his divisions as an aid to interpretation rather than quibbling about their precise terminology or seeking for their exact equivalents in mapping. To do otherwise might be to introduce unnecessary conflicts and confusions. The words 'primary' and 'secondary', for example, may convey the unacceptable assumption that there is a hierarchy of meanings, while in cartography 'natural' and 'conventional' are usually employed differently than in art history. The aim of Panofsky's divisions is, however, to reveal the hidden meaning in images and it is in this objective that their relevance for the history of cartography will be found.

Table 1. Iconographical parallels in art and cartography

ART (Panofsky's terms are used)	CARTOGRAPHY (suggested cartographic parallel)
1. Primary or natural subject matter: artistic motifs	individual conventional signs
2. Secondary or conventional subject matter	topographical identity in maps: the specific place
3. Intrinsic meaning or content	symbolic meaning in maps: ideologies of space.

(1) Primary or natural subject matter: conventional signs

This level of understanding consists of identifying 'pure forms' which were 'representations of natural objects such as human beings, animals, plants, houses, tools and so forth'[15]. These pure forms, or artistic motifs, are in Panofsky's words the carriers of primary or natural meaning. It is suggested that when looking at maps as opposed to pictures for his 'natural objects' there can be substituted landscape features, both physical and man-made, and for the artistic motif, the conventional sign. Thus in Saxton's county maps, the 'molehills' or 'sugar-loaves' used to represent hills, the clumps of trees standing for woodland, the palings for parks, and the single or grouped buildings to depict settlements, all communicate meaning at this 'level' of cartographical understanding. They are all icons of tiny fragments of landscape. In many cases they are mimetic signs[16], that is to say, bearing a visual resemblance to the features represented. This is why it is so hard to draw the line between landscape painting and cartography in the Renaissance, especially when the former employed the laws of perspective or exhibited the realism of seventeenth-century Dutch art.

In Tudor society, where maps were still a relatively novel form of representation, the mimetic character of many conventional signs on Saxton's maps and their derivatives must have facilitated their 'reading' in the manner of artistic motifs as defined above. It was not just a question, as some have implied, that mimetic signs could be more easily understood in a less sophisticated society than our own and that, rather like picture books for children, there subsequently occurred a graduation to real topographical maps.[17] The point is that Saxton's signs could function as a cartographic *lingua franca* helping to fashion mental geographies at a variety of territorial scales away from the limited 'eyewitness' experience of individual observers. Thus, although Saxton's maps are usually regarded as representations of identified places, when viewed outside the matrix of the particular map and a knowledge of the land it contained, their naturalistic signs derive their potency from the fact that they could be regarded as 'placeless'. Irrespective of where Saxton had located them on the map of England, they still had meaning. To an Elizabethan who had lived all his life in Surrey but was entirely ignorant of the geography of Northumberland, the fact that the latter county was depicted in the atlas of 1579 by means of hills, forests, rivers, towns, churches, and parks, *ipso facto* made it a more immediately credible landscape. The image, in short, mediated the features of the unknown county with the viewer's own experience of the English landscape. Places were transformed from a state of separation to one of proximity, and this viewer was placed 'inside' a countryside which would have otherwise been invisible to him.

Within this first stratum of the map image a map did not require Euclidean co-ordinates to have meaning. Nor is this limited to Tudor maps: this would be as true of the cartography of the century when triangulation was introduced into England, as it had been of the Hereford map in the thirteenth century. And in the late sixteenth century, the rivers, hills, cities, cornfields, and vineyards of the imaginary map of Utopia were expected to convey a recognised set of meanings which did not depend on the 'reality' of their geography and were comprehensible despite any possible allegorical allusion to London and the Thames.[18] Conventional signs placed thus on any sheet of paper (or indeed on other media) evoked landscape elements which were universal rather than particular, just as artistic motifs carried meanings independent from the specific composition within a picture.

(2) Secondary or 'conventional' subject matter: the specific place

Panofsky's example of this level of meaning, in the second stage in the procedure of interpretation, involves apprehending that a group of figures shown seated at a dinner table, the 'pure forms', exhibited a 'certain arrangement' and 'certain poses' which identify them as a representation of the Last Supper. Motifs at primary level have thus become carriers of secondary or 'conventional' meaning, at least to those familiar with the content of the Gospels. Some historians of art and culture have called this the 'manifest content' of a painting[19], and there is also an analogy to studies in literary criticism where this level would equate with the so-called literal or narrative meaning of the text.[20]

In cartographic interpretation the analogy can be direct and involves recognising that a particular spatial arrangement of conventional signs is intended to denote a specific place; for example, map x in Saxton's atlas is in fact a representation of Northumberland rather than of Surrey or Utopia. This stratum of meaning is probably the most tangible in terms of its amenability to historical reconstruction and it equates well with our established knowledge about the functional uses of maps – for defence, administration and wayfinding. It is this practical dimension of Renaissance carto-graphy which is most frequently commented upon by historians. J.R. Hale has written of the early sixteenth century, when 'only a minute fraction of Europe's population had ever seen a map', that

Without the habit of conceptualising space, a traveller going to war or work could not link his separate impressions to the nature of his route as a whole or extend them imaginatively to the unseen parts of the area through which he was passing; a man could not visualise the country to which he belonged; a landowner, unable to 'see' his properties as a whole was not concerned to concentrate his scattered holdings by sale or exchanges; a ruler, unable to 'see' his kingdom was not perturbed by bargaining away provinces that map-conscious generations were to see as essential to strategic frontiers; governments, informed by verbal descriptions, were unable to judge the resources in men and materials of their rivals; generals miscalculated their lines of communications and found it difficult to work to a systematic plan of operations. Certainly, in an age virtually without effective maps the bump of locality is likely to be well developed, and the hunt sharpened an eye for terrain and the judging of distance. If however, there is an air of confusion and improvisation about the diplomatic and military events of the period it is, at least in part, because men were literally unable to see their goals.[21]

There are parallels to the England of the early 1500s. But in the course of the sixteenth century, there were to be men who acquired a wide range of maps and plans to assist in this process of 'seeing' the land, and the use of these maps is documented in an impressive range of practical affairs.

Thus, to many Elizabethans the word 'map' denoted a type of graphic tool to be used in their everyday business and which had taught them to think spatially. That they themselves did perceive this meaning is well documented. So John Dee, who had contacts with nearly everyone of importance in the age and can be regarded as the 'leader of the Elizabethan Renaissance'[22], and who recognised cartography to be a contemporary source of *objets d'art,* also envisaged that men would collect and use maps to further their understanding of real places, as in the study of

things past, as battles fought, earthquakes, heavenly firings, and such occurences, in histories mentioned: thereby lively as it were to view the place, the region adjoining the distance from us, and such other circumstances: some other, presently to view the large dominion of the Turk: the wide Empire of the Muscovite: and the little morcel of ground where Christiandom (by profession) is certainly known . . . some other for their own journeys directing into far lands, or to understand other men's travels.[23]

Moreover, by the end of Elizabeth's reign it had been accepted in court circles that in forming plans of campaign 'Cards and Maps' were necessities for kings and even an imperfect map was better than none.[24] Every aspiring statesman should have 'a booke of the Mappes of England . . . and also a good descripcion of the Realm of Irelande'.[25] And, adding to this apparent consensus about the utility of cartography, George Owen, the Pembrokeshire historian, reports how Saxton's maps were

usual with all noblemen and gentlemen and daily perused by them for their better instruction of the estate of this realm touching the quantity, situation, forms and special places of note.[26]

Still at this practical level of real places – but now also bearing on their potency as symbols – it may be noted that maps quickly developed a special authority as scientific documents. This was partly based on the Renaissance respect for the classical period and the learning of men such as Ptolemy. Maps were seen as mirrors to reality and this in turn lent prestige to the image. William Cuningham, author of *The Cosmographical Glasse* (1559), followed Ptolemy's definitions and regarded maps as part of a 'discription of the face, and picture of th' earth, with her partes knowen, and of such things as are to it connected and ioyned'.[27] Maps, Cuningham is informing us, represent real geography. Whether at the scale of the cosmos, of the world, a continent, Great Britain, a single county, or of a town or estate, the acceptability of the cartographic message began to be coloured by a perception of its detailed accuracy in representing what was believed to be scientific or geographical truth. In England, as elsewhere, one symptom of this concern on a national scale was the attempt to employ mathematically constructed map projections,[28] while even on the local scale, at the level of the county or estate, cartographers (or their critics) began to debate the reliability of their maps and to assess the contribution of different instruments and techniques to the planimetrical accuracy of the final product.[29] Thus, although educated Elizabethans would still have recognised that maps and pictures belonged to the same family, with maps being 'a certaine imitation of paintinge', they were becoming increasingly conscious of images created 'according to the rules of Geometrie, and the Arte Perspectiue': eventually Elizabethan cartographers were given the task by society of creating a 'full finished similitude'.[30] Hakluyt could write in 1589 of 'both the olde imperfectly composed, and the new lately reformed Mappes,

Globes, Spheares, and other instruments of this Art'.[31] This new quality of scientific accuracy gave their maps a special utility and, inevitably, much of their meaning.

If this functional interpretation is accepted as a complete one – as many historians of cartography seem to have – then there would be no point in extending the present semantic traverse to encompass Panofsky's third level of meaning. But it is suggested that a generalisation based solely on practical function is inadequate to explain the role of maps in Tudor society. As soon as we start to expand from the narrow base of 'surveyed' maps and to consider the wider contexts in which map images were viewed in early modern England, then it becomes clear that cartography was also employed in the moral and social discourse of the times, and was being involved in the charting of intellectual landscapes and in a communication of theories which are only partly related to practical affairs. It is in the identification of this type of meaning that Panofsky's third iconographical level may have something to offer.

(3) Intrinsic or latent meaning: ideologies of space

The third level was concerned with the search for deeper meanings in works of art. This stage of semantic interpretation, for which the term iconology is reserved, seeks to establish the relationships between the philosophical, political and religious ideas in a society and the form and content of art.[32] These are the symbolical values of Cassirer,[33] sometimes called the latent content in art.[34] In literary criticism, the equivalent would be that stream of research which looks for metaphor and symbol in the 'pattern' below the level of the plot or character.[35] In cartography, it is now suggested, these strata, identified in the subject matter of various disciplines, also have an exact counterpart. Put simply, the interpretation is shifted from the reconstruction of real places as revealed in particular maps to a reconstruction of the ideological or symbolic undertones of images as they were understood by the cartographers, their patrons, or by individuals or groups in the society who came into contact with the image.

As an object of historical enquiry, the study of thought has a quality of elusiveness not usually attached to the literal layer of information in maps. Art historians have criticised the iconological approach, and have warned against the tendency that iconological interpretation will uncover more symbolic meaning in a work of art than was originally intended or perceived.[36] Yet as far as cartography is concerned this surely poses questions that are no more difficult than for painting and literature, where the third level has uncovered remarkable insights not only into the meaning of particular images but also into the processes by which art and literature were transformed in different societies. With maps, moreover, which are images of place, a useful starting point in the location of latent meaning can be with the symbolic associations of the actual objects of representation, the countries, cities or rural landscapes, which have been depicted. Once these associations have been recognised, which are also articulated in other forms and media than those of maps, it becomes an easier step to identify similar meanings in the cartographic records of those places.

In this context research on Italian town plans of the Renaissance, identifying both the symbolic meaning of the actual landscape and the transference of what is symbolised into the cartographic image, has some valuable pointers for English cartography in the same period. By 1500 Venice, for example, had already become a symbolic landscape in the European mind. There was the 'myth' of Venice, a complex of ideas and values, which represented a 'union or conjunction of society and place'. In the creation of the myth or image 'an ideological interpretation of selected facts had been formulated'[37] and it is but one step to see how the symbolic significance of the urban landscape and its Utopian attributes were articulated in contemporary maps which equally well communicate ideas as topographical facts. This translation of meaning from the physical into the paper landscape has been most convincingly demonstrated by Juergen Schulz in relation to Jacopo de' Barbari's map of Venice of 1500. Schulz proposes that Jacopo's map was 'a visual metaphor for the Venetian state' and for the humanist and mercantile values its image enshrined.[38] It will be argued here, in order to provide an initial illustration of iconological truth in Tudor cartography, that there was also more than literally 'meets the eye' in the town plans of Elizabethan England.

London, not surprisingly in view of its size, on the European scale of urban life, and of the aspirations of its citizens, provides the most obvious example. In sixteenth and seventeenth century plans of the city encapsulations can be detected of an element of myth reminiscent of the symbolisation of the Venetian values inherent in Jacopo de' Barbari's plan. At least part of the meaning conveyed by the plans of London (as perceived by contemporaries) also related to Renaissance ideals and the cartographers were likewise employing the naturalistic image of the city to demonstrate the way it shared the civilised values of other great European cities. A recent study has suggested that the so-called 'Copperplate map' of *c*1553–59 may in fact have been engraved to mark a special occasion, such as the coronation of Queen Elizabeth.[39] If this is the case, like the plan of Venice, it would have been a visual metaphor for the Renaissance virtues of the city rather than just a literal record of the layout of its bricks and mortar. Another signpost to the presence of this ideological content, the projection of London as the quintessence of growing national pride, is also found in the captions attached to maps of the Tudor city (pl. 6). A panel with an ornamental border on the 'Agas map' of *c*1562, for example, proclaims This antient and famous City of London . . . first founded by *Brute* the Trojan'. Still within the panel, there follows a eulogistic statement about its antiquity, about its size and flourishing condition, about its mercantile prosperity, and about its pre-eminence as the 'chief City' and 'head and chief Chamber of the whole Realm'; on another sheet a verse of similar intent begins 'New Troy my name'.[40] These glosses on the map were not designed to fill up blank spaces (indeed the cartographer may have deliberately suppressed topographical detail known, in one case, to be available to him, to accommodate the text on the image) but deliberately placed so as to direct the beholder's mind to the meaning of the image as a whole.

Lest it should be argued that London was an exceptional case, other examples can be cited. To give just one example, an iconological interpretation is found to apply equally well to Richard Lyne's map of Cambridge (1574). First, starting with the primary level, some of the individual conventional signs (largely mimetic in character) as well as the architectural drawings of the colleges carry a meaning probably independent of their positioning on the ground plan and in this sense they would have been comprehensible to a stranger quite unfamiliar with Cambridge's streets and alleys. Secondly, at the manifest or literal level, Lyne's map may be regarded as a straightforward topographical statement about Cambridge in 1574 (pl. 7). Like similar

Tudor town plans, it has been intensively used for this information by urban historians in reconstructing the 'real' geography of Tudor times.[41] Thirdly, however, it is also evident that Lyne's map was intended to be a visual metaphor for certain ideal qualities perceived in the University City. Even were we not aware of this from the map itself, with its many decorative features[42] doubtless flattering reality, it is explicit in the descriptive note in the top right hand corner:

Cambridge, a very famous city . . . immortalising the name and memory of the Founder, preserves a University dignity which is even more illustrious than that of old.[43]

The key words in this inscription – famous, immortal, dignity, illustrious and old – in the Renaissance, especially honorific words with symbolic connotations, were intended to convey not merely their literal sense but also the suffusion of their attributes over the spaces and buildings represented on the plan. In this example the map, assisted by its written captions, functioned as a symbol in the creation of the required myth. It was used to enhance a Utopian view of an ideal place which, although it may have been at variance with reality on the ground or with the authentic facts about the origin of the city or, yet again, with the practical uses to which the plan may have been put[44], was nevertheless of vital importance in the formulation of attitudes towards this particular English town.

To what extent can we generalise on the basis of these two examples? Do all maps, rather than just certain maps, carry a deeper meaning behind the 'factual' image of their geographical details? It would be impossible in the context of a short paper to rehearse the evidence in full but it may be suggested that many other categories of maps and plans in Tudor England also enshrine symbolic meanings and that they exercised comparable social functions to those described above for London and Cambridge. While their meanings are sometimes clarified by captions such as those on the plans of London and Cambridge, even without such qualification cartographic images were widely invested with symbolic meanings of an abstract nature. To assist in considering this proposition more systematically a classification has been devised (Table 2), setting out the practical uses of the main types of Tudor maps, together with examples of their symbolic meanings and of the associated social functions they exercised. As with art in general so, too, with the iconology of maps; such a classification requires the reconciliation of the abstract concepts held by individuals, groups or whole societies in early modern England, with a range of symbolic meanings which may extend through cartographic manifestations of special interests (the educated Elizabethan's interest in British history and antiquity for example) and through expressions of doctrines (such as the political theories attaching to the crown and the nation state) to world views (extending into the realm of cosmological ideas).[45] In the context of the history of cartography, however, greater structural clarity would seem to be gained not from simple iconological classification of abstract ideas, but from linking the several different meanings of each map type and arranging these as spatial units of ascending area and complexity. So, at one end of the scale, the iconology is concerned with the intrinsic meaning of local estate maps while at the other end it is concerned with the cosmological truths expressed in Renaissance diagrams of the universe. This therefore is the rationale of Table 2, put forward as the basis for discussion rather than as a definitive statement on the ideas and myths symbolised in Tudor cartography.

Table 2. Examples of Tudor maps as tools and symbols

MAP TYPE	PRACTICAL USES	SYMBOLIC MEANINGS	SOCIAL FUNCTION OF IMAGE
1. Estate plans	Administration of estate; enclosure; emparking; legal disputes	seigneurial authority; proprietorship; class; pride, attitudes towards landscape and discovery of nature	maintenance of social structure based on land; rise of absolutism; development of aesthetic consciousness
2. City and town plans	Improvement schemes; town extension; planning new towns; administration; fortification	the ideal city; antiquity, fame and celebration of cities; mercantile wealth; the power of cities	Utopian city planning; differentiation of town and country in social and political terms
3. County maps	Westminster bureaucracy; national defence; county administration; regional trade and way finding; 'decoration'	the county community	the identity of the county as a social unit; the development of regional society and culture; the intellectual discovery of England
4. National maps: England and Wales; Great Britain; The British Isles	Administration and defence at national level; education	the nation and the crown; patriotism; the political state	rise of the national consciousness; ethnocentrism; exercise of secular power
5. World and hemisphere maps, including globes	Planning overseas discovery, exploration, colonisation and trade; education	empire; the New World; science and the Liberal Arts	attitudes to conquest and exploration; the creation of world views; the Renaissance 'discovery of space'
6. Celestial cartography	Astronomy and scientific discovery of the universe; navigation	emblems for cosmographies and religious systems; the royal image	reinforcement or refutation of religious, magical, and scientific beliefs; astrology; devine right of monarchy

Ambiguity: some problems of interpretation of the symbolic meanings in Tudor maps

While the practical functions of Tudor maps are generally accepted by historians, a greater degree of difficulty can be anticipated regarding their latent or symbolic meaning. The literal geography that is contained in these maps can be traced almost mechanically; the parks of southern England have been so abstracted,[46] an urban hierarchy has been constructed in this way for early seventeenth-century Wales,[47] and the internal geography of Tudor towns has often been re-mapped from Speed's town plans.[48] But the contours of symbolic meaning, involving abstract ideas, sentiments, and value judgements, cannot be followed in the same way. Nor can they be measured so convincingly as can be the planimetric distortion on maps of Great Britain in this period,[49] nor scanned and classified with as much scholarly confidence as are the chainlines or watermarks within the paper on which they were printed. Meaning is not only an abstract quality but also in many cases it would have related to more generalised matters than those associated with topography. It should, however, be no more difficult to isolate the deeper meanings of a map (and to assess its social influence) than those of a picture. The problem is merely that the underlying assumptions and procedures are different. In the remainder of this essay some possible areas of ambiguity are discussed and examples are given of conjunctions of historical evidence where it might be possible to define latent meaning more precisely.

(1) Symbolism and symbol defined

In the first place, a definition of the word 'symbol' in the context of the history of cartography may be regarded as a general problem. It reflects the need for a more precise use of language in clarifying some of our assumptions.[50] Symbols are by definition mysterious but in relation to maps a starting point is afforded by the widely accepted usage that symbolism is the practice of signifying a thing by means of something else that stands for it – that something else being its symbol. The problem in cartography is that this cognitive process of substitution can be related to at least three aspects of maps. First, in much of the literature of the history of cartography, symbol is employed as a synonym for conventional sign.[51] This is not necessarily misleading but it points to a complication in Panofsky's scheme that the *individual* conventional sign – the equivalent of his artistic motif (Table 1) – can stand literally for an object in the landscape and, at the same time, as an 'independent' sign and irrespective of the geography in the map, it can also evoke deeper meanings. An obvious example would be Norden's sign for religious places. By substituting a circle surmounted by a cross for a pictorial image of the buildings in the landscape, Norden may have conveyed to some believers in Reformation England[52] something of the Christian poignancy of that symbol. In other cases, conventional signs may have reflected contemporary perceptions of landscape features. An example would be the 'sugar loaf' sign for hills on Saxton's maps. In technical terms – and especially given our modern pre-occupation with scientific progress in cartography – this sign is usually dismissed as crude and inaccurate. Even so, there have been occasions when such maps have been scrutinised in order to try to identify precisely which hills were included and to relate them to known beacons or boundary stones.[53] Such literal interpretations, however, seem doomed to make only partial sense if undertaken without an understanding of the contemporary perception of mountains. It has to be remembered that, to the early modern as well as to the medieval mind, mountains were often regarded as bleak, barren and inhospitable. People did not bother to explore them or paint them from nature[54] so why should cartographers trouble to record them in other but cursory fashion? In short, Saxton's hills reflect an attitude in Elizabethan England to part of the natural world: their apparently careless delineation connotes a set of values rather than a purely technical backwardness. Nor did society press the map-maker to solve the problem of relief depiction: there was no demand for such precision. In this way and in this example, topographical ambiguity might be part of the meaning but it also points to the need for further studies of conventional signs which are concerned not just with their literal equivalents and their diffusion from the Continent to the British Isles (although these can be difficult enough

1. Detail from a panoramic map of the river Scheldt from Rupelmonde to the island of Walcheren, 1468.

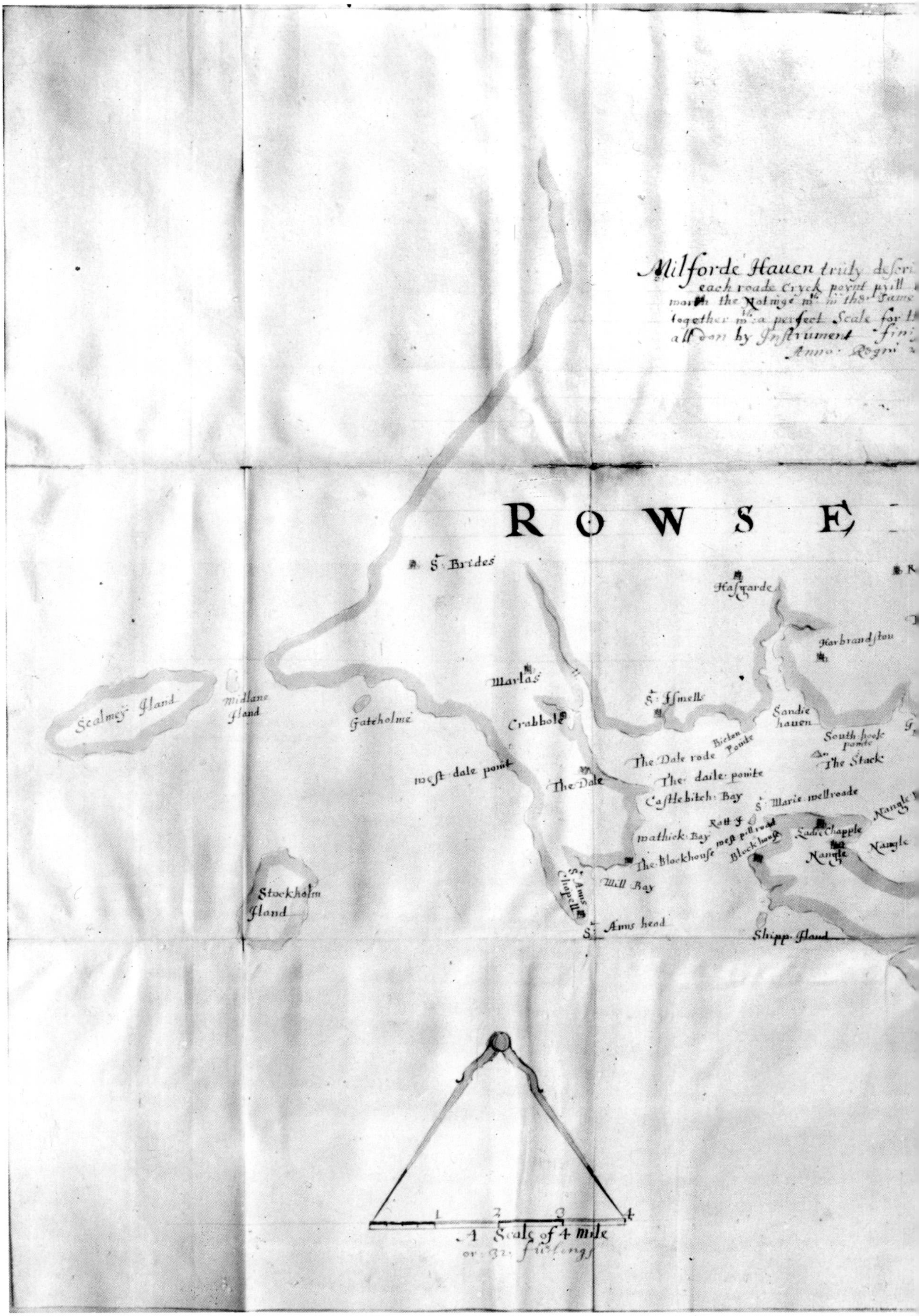

Milforde Hauen truly descri...
each roade cryck poynt pyll...
marsh the Notinge ... in the same...
together in a perfect Scale for...
all don by Instriument fin...
Anno Regni...

ROWSE

S. Brides

Hasgarde

Harbrandston

Scalmey Iland

midlane Iland

Marlas

S. Ismels

Sandie hauen

Gateholme

Crabbole

The Dale rode

Bicton Ponte

South hook ponte

west dale point

The daile ponte

The Stack

The Dale

Castlebitch Bay

S. Marie wellroade

mathick Bay

Roll f

west pillroad

Nangle f

The blockhouse

Blockhous

Ladie Chapple

Nangle

Stockholm Iland

S. Anns Chappell

Mill Bay

Nangle

S. Anns head

Shipp Iland

A Scale of 4 mile
or 32 furlongs

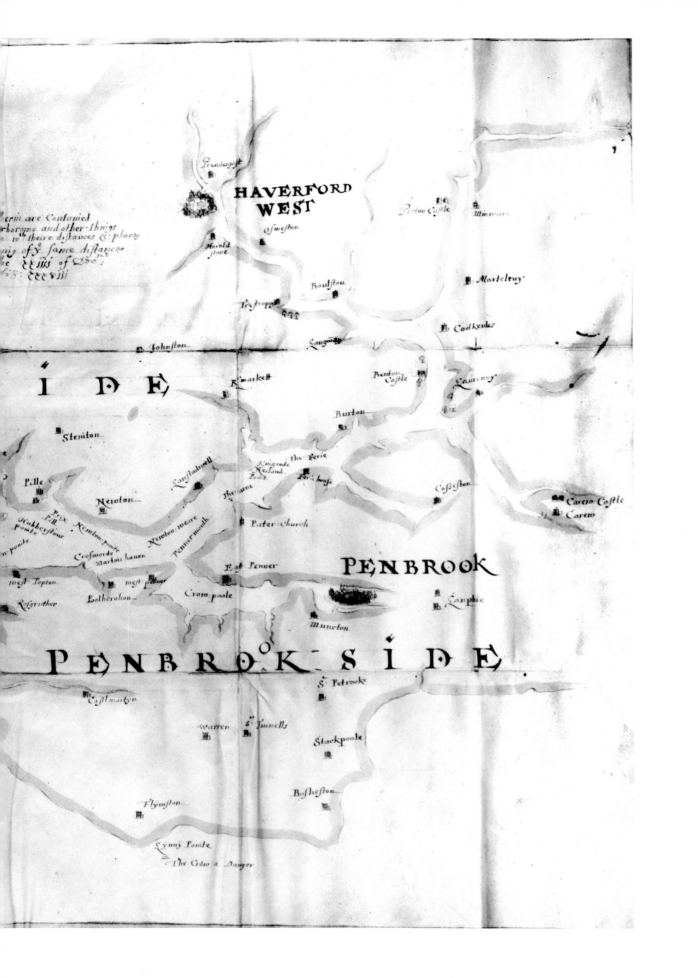

Prendergest

HAVERFORD
WEST

Picton Castle   Minware

Osmeston

...erin are Contained
...rboroes and other things
... w th theire distances & places
... ing of y e same distances
...ie ɛɛ iiii of Doe
...: ɛɛɛ viii

Harold
stone

Boulston   Marteltuy

Trestroppe

Cockxenles

Johnston   Longworth

IDE   K marskett   Benton   Laurenny
                                         Castle

                       Burton

Steniton

                                         the Ferie
                       Kingrode
Pille   Neiland   Lorz house
                        Point   Cosseston
Canstadwell   Carew Castle
                       The arne   Carew
Prix   Newton   Cosseston
Pill   Newton meare   Pater church
Hubberstone
pointe   Newlon mouth
        Crosworde   Martins haven   East Penner   PENBROOK
west Topton   west penner   Lamphie
    Roferother   Lootherohon   Crom poole   Muncton

PENBROK SIDE

                                 S t Petrooks
        Castlmartyn

              warren   S t Tunells
                                       Stackpoole

                              Bosheston
Flymston

    Lynny Pointe
      The Crow & Danger

A true and perfect Plott of all the Demefne Landes belonging to the Mannor of Garnetts, Scituate, lying and being in the feuerall Parrifhes of High Eafter, Donmowe Magna and Waltham Magna in the Countie of Elsex. Hauing the Priuiledg of keeping Courte Barron. With the proffitts and comodities thereunto beelonging of Free and Customarie lands. Vizٍ Quitt Rents, Releefes, Fynes, Waifes, Strayes, Deodants, Hawking, Hunting, Fishing, and Fowling &c. The Chappell, Manfion houfe and other tents, in their true places, and order. Euerie Gatehoufe, Barnes, Stables, Douehoufe, Orchards, Yardes, Gardens, high waies, Driftwaies, Ponds, Pathes, Pound, Stiles, Gates, Bridges, And euery particuler Fielde, Woods, Springs, Hedg-rowes, placed in their right Formes. With the Contents of Acres, Roodes, and Perches of euery Seuerall. As in this Plott most plainlie it doth appeare.

5. The description of North Walland, South
Walland and Dengemarshe, c1592: detail.

6. Middlesex described with the most famous cities of London and Westminster. From J. Speed, *Theatre of the Empire of Great Britaine* (1611), shows the same sense of pride in London as the national capital which had previously been articulated in its Tudor plans.

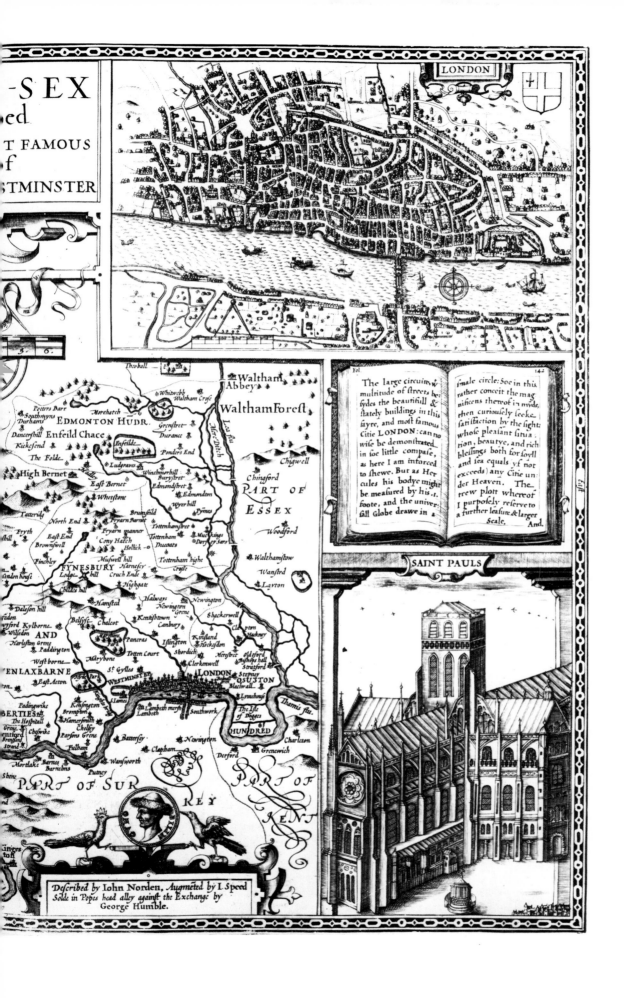

-SEX
ed

T FAMOUS
of
STMINSTER

LONDON

Fol. 142
The large circuit, w. multitude of ſtreets beſydes the beautifull & ſtately buildings in this ſayre, and moſt famous Citie LONDON: can no wiſe be demonſtrated in ſoe little compaſſe, as here I am inforced to ſhewe. But as Hercules his bodye might be meaſured by his .t. foote, and the univerſall Globe drawe in a

ſmale circle: Soe in this rather conceit the magnificens thereof in mvds, then curiouſly ſeeke ſatiſfaction by the ſight: whoſe pleaſant ſituarion, beautye, and rich bleſſings both for ſovll and ſea equals yf not exceeds) any Citie under Heaven. The trew plott whereof I purpoſely reſerve to a further leaſure & larger Scale.   And.

SAINT PAULS

Theoball

Waltham Abbey
Waltham Forest

Potters Barr
Southmyns
Durhams
EDMONTON HUDR.
Morehatch
Whitwch
Waltham Croſſe
Grenſtret
Durance

Dancershill
Kirkeſend
Enfeild Chace
Enfeilde
Ponders End

The Folde
Ludgraves
Winchmerhill
Buryſtret
Chigwell

High Bernet
Eaſt Bernet
Whetſtone
Edmondſtret
Chingford
PART OF
ESSEX

Tatteridg
North End
Brunsfeild
Fryarn Barnet
Fryarn manner
Wyerhill
Pymes
Woodford

Fryth
Eaſt End
Brownſwell
Cony Hatch
Tottenhamſtret
Muſkings
Dorſey Sore

Finchley
Muſwell hill
Hollick
Tottenham Ducoats
Walthamſtow

FYNESBURY
Lodge
hill
Harneſey
Cruch Ende
Tottenham highe
Croſſe
Wanſted

Childs hill
Highgate
Layton

Daleſon hill
Hamſted
Halways
Newington
Grene
Newington

Kylborne
Wilſdon
Belſſſe
Chalcot
Kentiſhtown
Canbury
Clapton
Hackney

Harleſton Grene
Paddington
Pancras
Iſlington
Kingland
Hockeſdon
Shackerwell

Weſtborne
Marybone
Totten Court
Sherdich
Mereſtret
Clerkenwell
Oldesford
Byſhops hall
Stratford

ENLAXBARNE
St Gylles
WESTMINSTER
LONDON
Stepney
Blackwall
QSUSTON

Padingwike
BERTIES
The Hoſpitall
Kenſington
Brompton
Hamerſmith
Chelſey
Lambeth merſh
Lambeth
Southwork
Lymehouſe
The Iſle of Dogges
HUNDRED
Thamis flu.

Chiſwike
Parſons Grene
Battersey
Newington
Derford
Grenewich
Charleton

Mortlake
Barnes
Barnelms
Wanſworth
Clapham
PART OF KENT

PART OF SUR REY

Shene

Deſcribed by Iohn Norden, Augmeted by I. Speed
Solde in Popes head alley againſt the Exchange by
George Humble.

7. Richard Lyne's map of Cambridge (1574) can be interpreted both in terms of its contemporary topography and as a metaphor for ideal qualities perceived in the University city.

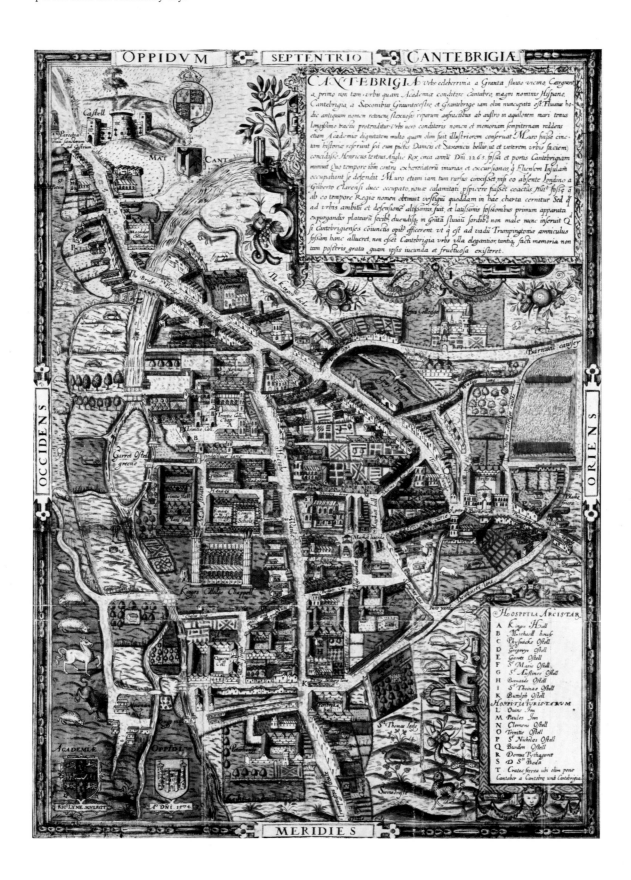

8. This portrait of Queen Elizabeth I *c*1592 by
Marcus Gheeraerts the younger employs the map of
England as a symbol interchangeable for Queen
and nation.

9. Detail showing conventional symbols from John Norden's map of Hampshire, MS *c*1595. This is one of the earliest examples of such an explanation on an English map.

10. William Leybourne in *The Compleat Surveyor* (1653) provided a general model for drafting estate plans but did not elaborate their conventional signs.

11. Detail from Samuel Walker's map of Garnetts, Essex, 1622, showing the manor house standing as an emblem of pride in property and ownership of the land.

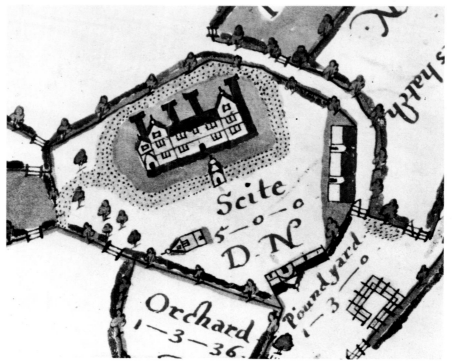

13. Detail from Ireland in J. Speed's *Theatre of the Empire of Great Britaine* (1611) indicating a social order among the inhabitants of Ireland which through the map would become associated with the country as a whole.

The Gentleman of Ireland   *The Gentlewoman of Ireland*

The Civill Irish Woman   *The Civill Irish man*

The Wilde Irish man   *The Wilde Irish Woman*

12. The identity of the architectural feature employed in the title cartouche from the plan of the East Field in Kessingland, Suffolk (by H.M., 1613), is not known but its careful integration in the map and the use of Latin in the title may have been intended to suggest the surveyors' learning or professional qualifications. Even where such symbols seem to have been included as a routine act of decoration their potential for wider communication should not be underestimated, *cf.* the deliberate alteration of decoration in plates 37a and b. apparently to suit eighteenth century sensibilities.

questions) but also with what meaning the cartographers themselves and their clients may have derived from individual motifs.[55]

A second way in which maps of the Tudor period operated as symbols is by means of their physical form. It could be the map itself, as an artefact, that became a symbol quite independently of the fact that it contained a direct portrayal of a specific geography or any other message. In these situations the map itself was a generalised metaphor. The most outstanding example of this was the widespread use of celestial and terrestrial globes. A globe or orb, held in the hand of a monarch, signified sovereignty over the world, and it was first used thus by the Roman emperors. Similarly, a terrestrial globe was widely associated with the personified virtues of the Liberal Arts and signified their universality.[56] One tangible measure of the symbolic significance of globes in the Renaissance is that they were sometimes constructed in precious metals instead of the ordinary wood frames and *papier-mâché* cover.[57] In Tudor England in particular, the use of terrestrial globes as artistic motifs in painting is well known through examples such as Holbein's portrait of *The Ambassadors*[58] but perhaps the most persistent use of this generalised cartographic image is to be found among the symbolic accoutrements depicted in portraits and other representations of Elizabeth I. The making of Elizabeth's image, a task which employed the visual arts as well as literature, ceremony and ritual, has been extensively studied in recent years. The Queen's advisers were clearly aware of the mnemonic power of the image[59] and Roy Strong, for example, has pointed to a whole cult of 'Elizabeth Gloriana', the 'Virgin Queen', and *'Eliza Triumphans'* in which the iconography was rich in classical motifs, prophesying the return of an Augustan age.[60] The idea of Empire played a vital part in the thought of the Tudor period. It was manifest in the nationalist drive to overseas expansion; it was rooted in the wider Renaissance conception of world-empire; and it was translated into an Elizabethan imperialism expressed in terms of royal supremacy over both church and state.[61] For all these aspects of the imperial legend, the globe was a standard symbol. In the Armada portrait (*c*1588) a globe is tipped at an angle towards the viewer, and its meaning is derived from the central figure of the Queen, whose imperial hand extends to grasp the whole world. The symbolic globe appears in other portraits, such as those of Sebastian Cabot and Martin Frobisher[62], or in that of Sir Henry Lee, Queen Elizabeth's champion at the tilt, where it is shown on his sleeves.[63] It also appears, together with maps, as a metaphor in the literature of the period.[64]

After the publication of Saxton's atlas in 1579 and its popularisation amongst the gentry, the map of England came to convey likewise allegorical meanings.[65] In the Ditchley portrait (*c*1592), by Marcus Gheeraerts the younger, Elizabeth stands with her feet planted on the map of England, the map symbolising the association between crown and nation (pl. 8). In the same portrait, a more universal dominion is suggested by the Queen wearing a pendant earring designed as an armillary sphere.[66] Such links between the Queen and the map of England or cosmological motifs are quite unmistakable in their meaning. They are also reflected in the quatrain which prefaces this paper and which celebrated the same occasion. Of course, during the seventeenth century, the symbolic use of maps as motifs in painting to represent *vanitas*, or worldliness, as well as political and military power and authority, became much more common, especially in Dutch art, but Gheeraert's picture shows how maps had already acquired abstract meanings in late sixteenth-century England. What is so important for the history of cartography are the wider implications of the artist's choice of these particular motifs. It seems a commonsense assumption that the symbolic meaning of the globes and maps was not confined merely to those examples of art where they actually appear. Indeed, the argument can be turned right round to suggest that a necessary condition for their employment by the artist would have been that they were generally understood by the patron or the potential viewers of the picture. The Imperial message must have been already widely communicated so that whenever men looked at a globe or map of England – whether in the schoolroom, library, or in the Queen's Gallery at the Palace of Whitehall – it would itself have evoked some of the same emotions as would their contemplation of the painting. The widespread use of globes and maps in emblematic title pages for atlases and other geographical works of the period similarly strengthened the commonly understood meanings of these cartographic artefacts.

The third dimension on which a map could operate as symbol was that of its specific geographical imagery. That the content of Tudor maps, identified in 'real' geographical terms, also conveyed meanings in Panofsky's deeper sense is shown in Table 2. Ideas such as those of Empire, the ideal city, or seigneurial authority were articulated through the image of the specific space and the particular place. Indeed, the realism of the image may have served to strengthen the force of symbolic as well as literal meanings. An example of the latter is the way the new scientific celestial cartography of the Renaissance continued to be harnessed for astrological purposes in Tudor England. Thus, in *The Ambassadors* portrait, an ordinary celestial globe is depicted; while it could have simply represented a set of astronomical observations,[67] it could also have been intended to carry an astrological meaning. This duality, however, serves to illustrate the difficulty of separating layers of meaning. Although astrology perpetrated 'unscientific' ideas, it nevertheless helped to popularise the new science, such as Copernican conclusions about the universe; moreover, the revival of English astrology in the second half of the sixteenth century was also closely linked with the rise of the applied mathematical sciences.[68]

Although each of the three levels can be defined to stand on its own, in practice all three dimensions were often united in particular communications. In the cartography of early modern England literal and metaphorical meanings are thus so closely intertwined[69] that simple interpretations (such as the equation between globe and empire in defined contexts) may turn out to be the exception rather than the rule. But if the very essence of symbols may lie in their manifold meaning, so great is the potential for ambiguity that it is important to clarify the conditions under which maps may be said to convey a symbolic meaning. In some cases the symbolic content of the maps will be a direct transference of the meaning of features in the landscape which themselves have clearly defined symbolic connotations. It is fairly obvious, for example, that Tudor plans of Stonehenge replicated and reinforced the myths associated with that monument.[70] Similarly, contemporary large-scale plans of geometrical gardens laid out in the form of the cosmos – such as the Ptolemaic universe showing the earth in the centre encompassed by the spheres of the planets[71] – also carried the meaning of that design in general. Yet another example is the Renaissance diagrams of garden mazes of one kind or another. Mazes anciently symbolised death and have been said to represent maps of the underworld, showing the route to be taken by the departing spirit[72] while another interpretation is that the labyrinth is a 'microcosm of the earth and a macrocosm of the human anatomy'.[73] This latter analogy, between the human body and the country as a whole, was also a familiar one in early modern England.[74] More often than not, however, the concepts conveyed by cartographic imagery were less specific. The particular meaning of the map images is only established through a rather elusive conjunction of evidence for certain social, political and religious associations. This type of interpretation requires more detailed knowledge both of the 'code' employed by map-makers and of the 'context' of the transmission of meaning and its reception in Tudor society.

(2) The code of Tudor maps

The terms code, discussed here, and context, discussed in the following section, are borrowed from linguistics, where they have been recognised as two of the constituent elements within the structure of speech.[75] The argument here is not that maps communicate their deeper meaning in the same way as written language or speech but that some of the historical conditions under which they do so may be regarded as analogous.[76] It is not intended to suggest that the use of the term 'code' in a history of cartography context implies any automatic or pre-determined relationship between meaning and the manner of its expression.[77] If, however, the term is taken to refer to all marks composing the map image – conventional signs, written captions, place-names, the decorative or non-topographic elements of its design, for instance – it will be found to be a helpful metaphor. In order to understand the symbolic message or meaning of a map, it is necessary to reconstruct both the code employed by the map-maker and the precise historical context in which it was used. Two main problems are encountered, however, in attempting to extricate the symbolic meanings of Tudor maps from the various elements constituting this 'code', the meaning of the individual signs and the possible existence of messages within the decorative elements of the code.

The problem of the meaning of individual conventional signs involves treating this aspect of its total meaning as a discrete entity. It has already been suggested that iconic conventional signs could have functioned much as a *lingua franca*. They would have provided a mimetic representation of landscape features which could be universally comprehended and communicate across the great social divide of literacy. Yet not all conventional signs are iconic representations of landscape features. Some were designed to represent invisible attributes of places such as administrative status or boundaries and at this point, therefore, the idea that even a naturalistic cartography could have spoken to all men needs careful examination. On the one hand, towards the end of the sixteenth century at least some English map-makers, notably William Smith and John Norden, believed that topographical maps required a legend or characteristic sheet to explain their conventional signs (pl. 9).[78] On the other hand, it has to be admitted that while other aspects of cartography – notably surveying – were explained in great detail in contemporary treatises, the manner in which details were to be expressed, the cartographic code, seems to have been taken for granted (pl. 10). In the seventeenth as well as the sixteenth century, the writers of these textbooks appear to have been more concerned with the colour code recommended to map-makers than with the increasing mutations of signs[79], nor was there any theoretical discussion of the content or design of these signs. Indeed, in this respect the new cartography of the Renaissance lagged behind the older art of painting where, although there was a widely understood language of artistic motifs, such was the multiplicity of meaning attaching to individual symbols and personifications that dictionaries such as Cesare Ripa's *Iconologia* (1593) were regarded as necessary to unravel the meanings of many kinds of visual designs.[80]

The second problem in extricating meaning from the Tudor map code is that historians of cartography have neglected an important aspect of that code – its decorative content – in favour of concentration on the central geographical image (pl. 12). To read many authorities on the subject of decoration is to be informed that such embellishment is largely peripheral to the main purpose of the map, and that it obfuscates 'true' geography. Even Edward Lynam, whose understanding of Tudor cartography was profound, remarks of the maps in Saxton's atlas that they are 'almost an example of decoration for decoration's sake, for scientific cartography had still far to go'.[81] This view was echoed by R.A. Skelton when he wrote, almost as an apology for the map-maker, that

Until the 18th century, the map-maker was handicapped by many deficiencies of knowledge and technique . . . But, if these constraints reduced the scientific usefulness of his map, they offered the cartographer a larger field in which to exercise his sense of fitness in design and pattern, his ingenuity in ornament, and even his fancy.[82]

It is surely high time that this superficial, 'ornamental' view of decoration on Tudor maps is superannuated. It is an attitude based on the notion that decoration is a marginal exercise in aesthetics in contradistinction to the central map image, which is in the proper business of communicating 'hard' information. There is a 'frontier between ornament and symbol'[83] which has been much debated by historians and philosophers of art.[84] A more satisfactory interpretation, however, which will also assist in capturing an important aspect of cartographic meaning which has hitherto slipped through our fingers, is to regard both decorative and geographical images on a map as unified parts of a total image. It is true that some Elizabethans did believe in decoration on maps as a means to aesthetic pleasure[85] but this concept should now be enlarged to one in which decoration is seen to have served moral, religious, educational or political ends if not geographical ones. In cartography, the decoration qualified the images of landscape or territory and added value to the literal geographical statement in a variety of ways.

Tudor and seventeenth century cartography provides numerous examples of the way these social functions of decoration were allied to the images in maps (pl. 13). As well as stimulating the fancy and imagination, in many cases decoration lent ideological support to the meanings identified in Table 2. On Saxton's general map of England and Wales in the atlas of 1579, for example, just as in the great wall map of 1583, the rich decoration was not a commercial exercise in filling up blank spaces (as cynics, from Jonathan Swift onwards, have implied), but is part of that celebration and deliberate mystification of an English empire and golden age already referred to. Lynam was much closer to the truth when he wrote that 'Saxton deserves a place beside Shakespeare as an interpreter of the national consciousness, unity and pride which were the greatest achievements of Elizabethan England'.[86] Even if 'achievement', in such literal terms, is queried it remains probable that the images provided by Saxton were manipulated for these ends. On Saxton's map, the royal arms, Neptune, the fruits of the land and sea, the birds and flowers, the galleons and merchant vessels surrounding *Anglia*, and added to individual county maps, all help to articulate this myth of national pride and unity. The difficulty is to see today as things were then, but if this was indeed the total impression conveyed by the map in Tudor times, those contemporaries well versed in symbolism would have found the individual motifs plucking a variety of chords in this ethnocentric fugue of a map.

Much the same can be said about the decoration of other maps of the period. With Speed's *Theatre* we are informed explicitly that the work was patriotically inspired by 'the zeale of my countries glory' and its Preface is a eulogy for 'the very Eden of Europe'.[87] Like Speed's *History*, his maps were designed to proclaim an ideological belief about his country, about the course of its history, and about its political system and destiny. Moreover, like Camden, Speed's aim was 'to acquaint the world with the ancient state of Britain . . . to restore Britain to Antiquity and Antiquity to Britain'.[88] Thus the Roman antiquities and coins, the scenes of battles, the portraits of kings and queens, the arms of noble families, the plans of 'famous and fayre Cities' – all contribute co-ordinates to a set of values which Camden, Robert Cotton and their circle had earlier lent intellectual authority.[89] In this case, the marginalia are highlighting the well-known Renaissance enthusiasm for the civilisation of the classical world.[90] They also confirm how this was an emotion felt as well by educated men in seventeenth-century England. So in Speed's atlas, theirs was a country where Romans, Saxons, and Danes had fought over its space, while the landscape held a series of signposts to the destroyed monastic era[91] and in this way the cartographic images helped project a sense of time as well as of place into the landscape. Such visual metaphors as those employed by Speed cannot be ignored. On the one hand they connected the world of historical ideas with the contemporary landscape, linking the concrete and the abstract which are never far apart in maps. On the other hand, Speed's maps, besides manifesting the Renaissance discovery of England's past and conveying its sense of history, also gave support to the geo-political doctrines of his day.[92]

Even some of the smaller fragments of English Tudor cartography – especially the growing number of large-scale estate maps – can be reinterpreted along the same lines and their meanings read by deciphering their codes at two levels. Thus at one level they represent straightforward topographical inventories, itemising fields, land use, settlement patterns and form, ownership and tenancy. In this connection, as it is well documented, they become part of the mechanisms of enclosure and litigation.[93] But at the deeper level, an estate map, often with its view of the manor house, was also a seigneurial emblem, asserting the lord of the manor's legal power within the rural society. For him, the map was one badge of his local authority. Family coats of arms added within the margins were certainly for him more than mere decoration, for the right to these heraldic emblems also incorporated an individual's right, rooted in the past, to the possession of land.[94] Other artistic motifs, even where primitively executed, symbolised other rights, experiences or emotions also connected with the territory which had been mapped. So hunting scenes represented a specific privilege of landowners, and the depiction of houses and buildings stood for a pride in the ownership of that property (pl. 11). Could yet another theme have been a humanist sensibility to the sights and fragrance of nature? The animals, birds, fruits, flowers, and trees which decorate so many English estate plans may be again more than mere embellishment, serving rather to qualify and to enrich the patron's association of landscape.[95] Tudor estate plans were thus performing a variety of social functions. They were fostering an almost poetic sense of attachment to place while simultaneously reinforcing concepts of lordly power over the peasant communities where these estates extended.

(3) The context of Tudor maps

Students of language have long insisted that context is all-important in the interpretation of meaning. Their argument has been summarised as follows:

the message must refer to a *context* understood by both addresser and addressee, which enables the message to make 'sense' . . . the 'message' does not and cannot supply all of the 'meaning' of the transaction, and . . . a good deal of what is communicated derives from the context . . . 'Meaning' in short resides in the *total* act of communication.[96]

In the context of the history of cartography 'map image' may be substituted for 'message', 'map-maker' for 'addresser', and the 'particular beholder of the map' for 'addressee'. The sequence is an oversimplification because, as with Saxton's atlas, the simple 'map-maker' is shorthand for several craftsmen while behind each cartographer there would have been a supporting cast of national patrons and county officials. Yet even in this simplified form the role of context in the elucidation of meaning can be firmly established.

A priori, the identification of differing historical contexts enables us to infer (or at least to search for evidence for the contention) that an almost identical geographical image in a map can have subtly varied meanings. There is, first of all, the total circumstance of a particular work. For instance, the image of Northumberland in the maps of Saxton and Speed respectively, may have conveyed quite different meanings according to the different contexts of those two atlases. The two images are 'geographically' similar as regards delineation of hills, rivers, coasts, etc., but in one atlas the maps stand as independent folio sheets while in the other they were presented as illustrations to a text which was historical in emphasis and which channelled the thoughts of map users towards a particular set of meanings. E.H. Gombrich's dictum, that there should be a 'priority of context over expression in the theory and practice of interpretation',[97] seems to be particularly relevant in such cases.

In establishing the overall meaning of an atlas, the titlepage – especially if it is an emblematic titlepage made up of a complex of images – tends to be overlooked. Yet it may provide a key to the context as this was understood both by the map-maker and his patrons. On the frontispiece of Saxton's atlas, to take a well-known example, there is grouped a series of artistic motifs in a tableau around the figure of Queen Elizabeth. Her setting is an architectural one, perhaps suggesting a triumphal arch, and her pose is reminiscent of some Madonna in a picture of the Italian Renaissance. The flanking figures add to this meaning, with representations of Geography and Astronomy. In a smaller panel beneath, there is a man drawing a map of England (surely Saxton in spirit if not in likeness) and another taking astronomical observations with a telescope.[98] It may be noted that the iconography of the titlepage plays its spotlight more on Elizabeth herself than on the cartographic elements, which again suggests how quickly Saxton's maps had been pressed into ideological as well as into practical use. Saxton's atlas is by no means a unique example. Similarly emblematic titlepages pinpoint in the same way the context and tone of the mapping which follows. The titlepage of Speed's *Theatre* (1611–12), for instance, despite its reference to 'An Exact Geography', is evidently as much concerned with the substance of Britain's history and political status as with 'real' geography and landscape (pl. 14). Indeed, when Speed named his atlas *The Theatre of the Empire of Great Britaine*, the name was a direct imitation of Ortelius's *Theatrum Orbis Terrarum* (1570 and later editions) of which an English edition, with the title *The Theatre of the World,* had been published in 1606. The Latin word *orbis*, literally 'the world', also symbolised the authority of the Roman Empire, now attaching by implication to the English Empire. In the case of Drayton's *Poly-olbion, or a chorographical Description of Great Britain* (1612–22), the titlepage (pl. 15) which shows a virginal Albion wrapped in a cloak which is decorated as if it were a map, possibly to suggest the map of England,[99] reminds us that the 'literary' maps which follow, on which are positioned numerous allegorical figures, were intended to have a serious historical context and a specific role in the fashioning of antiquarian thought about the English countryside (pl. 16).[100] They were certainly not intended as mere 'cartographical curiosities'.

There is, secondly, the circumstances into which maps may have been placed by their individual users and by the market for maps. Again these contexts, in which customers came to use maps, may be different from those intended by the original creators of the maps. In the last third of the sixteenth century there occurred an especially rapid proliferation of the contexts, the formats and the media of mapping. It can be demonstrated how after the publication of Saxton's atlas in 1579, to take a single example, the county and national maps from that atlas were quickly reprinted, copied, re-edited, and reduced in order to fulfil new roles as illustrations in books (as for Camden and Speed), as diagrams in almanacks and travellers' guides, as curiosities in cabinets of wonder, as household tapesteries, and even as images on sets of playing cards. Thus, in printed cartography at least, while the image of the nation and of its regions was being gradually disseminated beyond the narrow circle of the Court and the gentry, the potential for divergent interpretations of the original image was greatly enhanced. The received meaning of maps was not always the meaning intended by the map-maker or by his patron and it is dangerous to infer meaning solely from the original function of the cartographic genre. To Lord Burghley, Saxton's maps were a tool of administrative control; cartographic knowledge was power and therefore eagerly seized upon by the principal statesman of a centralising government.[101] Yet in the hands of the gentry, distant from the ethos of Elizabeth's court, the very opposite effect might have been induced. In this other context, as Victor Morgan has noted, Saxton's maps would have served to shape and to reinforce that sense of identity and independence, summed up in the phrase the county community, for which historians have found so much evidence in relation to early modern England.[102] Similar permutations of context and meaning could be almost indefinitely extended to other types of maps and their users. Notwithstanding such variations, however, it seems likely that the use to which maps were put, coupled with reconstructions of the social attitudes and priorities of their users, will emerge as key factors in future historical studies of the meaning of maps. Such studies will also involve an empirical examination of their specific contexts – in private libraries, in geographical education at both artisan and elite levels, in published and unpublished treatises, and in literature and art – so that the 'historical geography' and the intensity of the different images can be assessed.[103] Only then, when the co-ordinates of map use have been more firmly fixed from independent non-cartographic knowledge, will it be possible to generalise about the wider significance of the rise of mapping in Tudor England.

Conclusion

Historians of cartography who accept that cartography is concerned with communication can hardly fail to be interested in meaning, for what is any language except a means of communicating intentions or meaning? It has been suggested in this essay that an iconographical approach derived from art history and linked to a linguistic concern for the historical codes and contexts of mapping, has much to offer in assembling a theory of cartographic meaning. To borrow John Berger's phrase, what is being sought are 'new ways of seeing' maps,[104] having regard for the semantic unity of the image as a whole and for the full historical circumstances surrounding its use. Despite the complexity of the boundary between convention and realism what emerges above all from this interrogation is that in Tudor England maps were often culture symbols; accordingly, they offer insight into the shared meanings, attitudes and values of that society and of some of the individuals which comprised it. The ability of maps to represent a wide range of ideas, as well as topographical facts, associated with land and territory gives rise to what has been defined as their social function and, in considering the wider historical role of cartography in early modern England, this must now be added to its better-known practical functions. In this process of communicating symbolic messages, maps reveal themselves to be a remarkably versatile language, operating in diverse contexts and at a flexible range of territorial scales. The effect of technical developments in cartography on this message-carrying capacity can also be reviewed. Accurately surveyed maps, because of scientific status, better instruments or Euclidean geometry, did not cease to be symbols in the manner which has been defined. Art and cartography did not 'split'[105] but rather more realistic images, appealing to the Renaissance sense of method and rationality, became even more potent and convincing as symbols of territory. The availability of printing techniques which overcame a major 'road-block' in communication through cartography and which in relative terms facilitated the mass production of 'exactly repeatable pictorial statements'[106], also greatly enhanced the potential social impact of maps. For Tudor England there is no better illustration of this social impact than Saxton's surveys and these surveys remind us how brilliant technical achievements can often have unexpected social consequences. Saxton was a technical instrument of government policy under Elizabeth but after 1579 he had little control over the images he had helped to create, that is to say over their meaning. Their scales could be changed, their media substituted, their contexts varied; they could be plagiarised, popularised, vulgarised, or used in political polemics at the will of others. Cartographic history has tended to stop at the moment the craftsman steps aside and the image is born into the world. But this is where the social history of cartography begins and the meaning of maps – despite the many ambiguities of its subject matter and its requirement for testable procedures – points the way to a still neglected aspect of Tudor cartography.

Acknowledgments

Versions of this paper were given as seminars in the Department of Geography, University of Liverpool, and in the *Occasional Discussions in Historical Geography* in Emmanuel College, Cambridge. I am grateful for constructive criticism in those places and also for other helpful suggestions received from John Andrews, Mark Cleary, Paul Harvey, Roger J.P. Kain, and David Woodward.

1. Quoted by R. Strong, *The Cult of Elizabeth: Elizabethan Portraiture and Pageantry* (London, 1977), p. 154 from George Peele's opening lines describing Sir Henry Lee's retirement tournament of 1590. For the fuller context, see *The Works of George Peele* edited by A.H. Bullen (London, 1888), II, pp. 281–301.

2. See S. Tyacke and J. Huddy, *Christopher Saxton and Tudor Map-Making* (London, 1980) for a resumé of current research directions.

3. An exception, stressing the inter-relationship of maps with society, is V. Morgan, 'The Cartographic Image of "The Country" in Early Modern England', *Transactions of the Royal Historical Society*, 5th ser., 29 (1979), 129–154; also V. Morgan, 'Lasting Image of the Elizabethan Era', *The Geographical Magazine*, 52 (1980), 401–408.

4. The question of definition is important here and it is proposed that the following definition be adopted: 'The map image is a structured . . . representation of selected spatial information, which when placed onto a storage medium becomes a map'. It is derived from *The Dictionary of Human Geography*, edited by R.J. Johnston (Oxford, 1981); for a discussion of the importance of an adequate definition of the word 'map' for the history of cartography, with implications for this paper, see M.J. Blakemore and J.B. Harley, 'Concepts in the History of Cartography . . . Questions of Definition', *Cartographica*, 19 (1982), pp. 82–85.

5. H. Whitaker, 'The Later Editions of Saxton's Maps', *Imago Mundi*, 3 (1939), 72–86.

6. E.H. Gombrich, *Symbolic Images. Studies in the Art of the Renaissance* (London, 1972), p. 2.

7. In general see A.H. Robinson and B.B. Petchenik, *The Nature of Maps. Essays toward Understanding Maps and Mapping* (Chicago, 1976); for a discussion of 'early maps as language' see M.J. Blakemore and J.B. Harley, 'Concepts in the History of Cartography: a Review and Perspective,' *Cartographica*, 17, no. 4, monograph, 26 (1980), pp. 87–106.

8. Semiotics or semiology has been defined as the 'science of signs': see T. Hawkes, *Structuralism and Semiotics* (London, 1977), for a discussion of the application of its ideas to a variety of disciplines.

9. Even in art history the two terms tend to be used interchangeably and without standardisation. Generally speaking, however, iconography has been taken to refer to the straightforward identification of images and iconology to the exegesis of their deeper meaning in the modern sense, as developed by Panofsky and others and as employed in this paper. See *The Oxford Companion to Art* edited by H. Osborne (Oxford, 1970) for brief distinctions. A much fuller methodological account appears in *The World Encyclopaedia of Art* 15 vols (1958).

10. In Blakemore and Harley, 'Concepts in the History of Cartography: a Review and Perspective' (1980) pp. 76–86; also J.B. Harley, 'The iconology of early maps', in *Acts of IXth International Conference on the History of Cartography*, edited by C. Marzoli (Institute of the Italian Encyclopaedia, forthcoming).

11. E. Panofsky, *Studies in Iconology. Humanistic Themes in the Art of the Renaissance* (Oxford, 1939).

12. E. Panofsky, *Meaning in the Visual Arts* (New York, 1955), p. 26.

13. For a recent indication of this attitude see R. Rees, 'Historical Links between Cartography and Art', *Geographical Review*, 70 (1980), 61–78, where he refers to the 'informal, prescientific phase of cartography' and that subsequently 'science claimed cartography'. Some art historians have also accepted such a transition from art to 'diagrammatic mapping': see E.H. Gombrich, 'The Visual Image', *Scientific American*, 227, no. 3 (1972), 82–96, especially p. 91: Doubtless there were some Renaissance cartographers who began to believe that pictorialism and accuracy were incompatible, but the argument here is also about how their contemporaries perceived and understood these maps even when superficially there was a decline of 'artistic' content.

14. An interesting confirmation of this assertion comes from the fact that modern artists frequently use maps as subjects or as artefacts in their painting. D. Woodward, 'Introduction' in *Cartography and Art* edited by D. Woodward (Chicago, forthcoming) cites the work of Piet Mondrian, and a number of recent artists in this context. For the Renaissance period see Samuel Y. Edgerton Jr, *The Renaissance Discovery of Linear Perspective* (New York, 1975), p. 113 who rather than identifying a schism between cartography and art, points at a 'parallel . . . between Ptolemaic cartography and the ideals of art in the fifteenth century'.

15. Panofsky, *Meaning in the Visual Arts*, p. 28.

16. See Robinson and Petchenik, pp. 61–65, for discussion and definitions.

17. Robinson and Petchenik, p. 61 observe that 'The ratio of arbitrary to mimetic marks on maps also increases as a society becomes more sophisticated'. The same distinction in relation to the history of topographical mapping is made by P.D.A. Harvey, *The History of Topographical Maps: Symbols, Pictures and Surveys* (London, 1980) where mimetic conventional signs are associated with the 'picture-map' as a stage of cartographic development.

18. C. Kruyfhooft, 'A Recent Discovery: Utopia by Abraham Ortelius', *Map Collector*, 16 (1981), 10–14.

19. P. Burke, *Tradition and Innovation in Renaissance Italy. A Sociological Approach* (London, 1974), pp. 179–206.

20. R. Weimann, *Structure and Society in Literary History:*

Studies in the History and Theory of Literary Criticism (London, 1977), p. 188.

21. J.R. Hale, *Renaissance Europe 1480–1520* (London, 1971), pp. 52–53.

22. F.A. Yates, *The Occult Philosophy in the Elizabethan Age* (London, 1979) pp. 79–87.

23. John Dee, Preface to *The Elements of Geometrie* (London, 1570).

24. *Theorique and Practise of Warre. Written to Don Philip Prince of Castil, by Don Bernardino de Mendoza. Translated out of the Castilian tonge into Englishe, by S' Edward Hoby, Knight. Directed to S' George Carew, Knight* (1597); quoted in E.M. Tenison, *Elizabethan England: being the History of this Country 'In Relation, to all Foreign Princes'* (Leamington Spa, 1953–.), x(1953), 190–91.

25. Robert Beale, 'A Treatise of the Office of a Councellor and Principall Secretarie to her Majestie', 1592; quoted in C. Read, *Mr Secretary Walsingham* (London, 1925) 1, 428–29; for an example of the use of maps in this context see J.H. Andrews, 'Geography and Government in Elizabethan Ireland' in *Irish Geographical Studies* (Belfast, 1970) pp. 178–191. For a wider discussion of the use of maps in overseas colonisation and subsequently in the writing of Raleigh's *History of the World* see R.A. Skelton, 'Ralegh as a Geographer', *Virginia Magazine of History and Biography*, 71 (1963), 131–49.

26. B.G. Charles, *George Owen of Henllys: A Welsh Elizabethan* (Aberystwyth, 1973) pp. 151–59.

27. William Cuningham, *The Cosmographical Glasse.* (London, 1559). On maps of the cosmos, including those of Cuningham, see S.K. Heninger Jr, *The Cosmographical Glass. Renaissance Diagrams of the Universe* (San Marino, California, 1977).

28. W.L.D. Ravenhill, 'Projections for the Large General Maps of Britain, 1583–1700', *Imago Mundi*, 33 (1981), 21–32; J. Keuning, 'The History of Geographical Map Projections until 1600', *Imago Mundi*, 12 (1955), 1–24.

29. Edward Worsop, *A Discoverie of Sundrie Errours and Faults Daily Committed by Landemeaters* (London, 1582); Ralph Agas, *A Preparative to Platting of Landes and Tenements for Surveigh* (London, 1596); John Norden, *Nordens Preparative to his Speculum Britanniae* (London, 1596).

30. Agrippa of Nettesheim, *De incertitudine et vanitate scientiarum* (1530; English edition, London, 1569); quoted by H.M. Wallis, 'Early Maps as Historical and Scientific Documents', in *Papers of the Nordenskiöld Seminar on the History of Cartography and the Maintenance of Cartographic Archives*, edited by K. Hakulinen and A. Peltonen (Helsinki, 1981) pp. 101–116.

31. Richard Hakluyt, *Principall Navigations* (London, 1589) quoted by R.A. Skelton, 'Hakluyt's maps' in *The Hakluyt Handbook* edited by D.B. Quinn (London, 1974), 1, 49.

32. Panofsky, *Meaning in the Visual Arts*, p. 30.

33. As identified by E. Cassirer, *The Philosophy of Symbolic Forms*, 3 vols (New Haven, 1953–57) vol. 1, *passim*.

34. Burke, p. 194.

35. Weimann, p. 188.

36. Panofsky, *Meaning in the Visual Arts*, p. 32, himself admitted to the 'danger that iconology will behave, not like ethnology as opposed to ethnography, but like astrology as opposed to astrography.

37. D. Cosgrove, 'The Myth and the Stones of Venice: an historical geography of a Symbolic Landscape', *Journal of Historical Geography*, 8 (1982), 145–69.

38. J. Schulz, 'Jacopo de' Barbari's View of Venice: Map Making, City views, and Moralized Geography before the year 1500', *Art Bulletin*, 60 (1978) 425–74. For a more literal but probably anachronistic interpretation see J.G. Links, *Townscape Painting and Drawing* (London, 1972), p. 87, who writes of the plan being 'for the enlightenment of the many business men who needed to visit Venice and find their way around it'.

39. J. Fisher, Introduction to *A Collection of Early Maps of London 1553–1667* (Lympne Castle, Kent, 1981). As R. Ashton, *The City and The Court 1603–1643* (Cambridge, 1979) demonstrates it is likely that such a map was also emblematic of more worldly ties.

40. The legend derived from Geoffrey of Monmouth, who stated that in very ancient times a mythical being called Brutus, a Trojan and a relative of the pious Aeneas who founded Rome, founded London as Troynavant, or New Troy, and from him were descended the British kings. Although untrue, this was part of the Tudor myth and a matter of national pride: K. Sharpe, *Sir Robert Cotton 1586–1631: History and Politics in Early Modern England* (Oxford, 1979) p. 25, points out that it tended to be adhered to even when it compromised standards of scholarship.

41. R.A. Skelton, 'Tudor Town Plans in John Speed's *Theatre*', *Archaeological Journal*, 108 (1952), 109–120, where he stresses the originality and reliability of the plans; also M.D. Lobel, 'The Value of Early Maps as Evidence for the Topography of English Towns', *Imago Mundi*, 22 (1968) 50–61.

42. T. Campbell, *Early Maps* (New York, 1981), reproduces in colour a superbly decorated presentation copy to King James (BL C.24.a.27.).

43. J.W. Clark and A. Gray, *Old Plans of Cambridge 1574 to 1798*, Part I: *Text* (Cambridge, 1921), p. 2, whose translation is followed.

44. Clark and Gray, p. 3, suggest that the plan may have been used in connection with schemes to secure a supply of wholesome water for Cambridge.

45. G. Hermerén, *Representation and Meaning in the Visual Arts. A study in the methodology of iconography and iconology* (Lund, 1969) pp. 126–151, sets out a logical basis for these types of distinction within iconological symbolism.

46. F.V. Emery, 'England *circa* 1600' in *A New Historical Geography of England before 1600* edited by H.C. Darby (Cambridge, 1976), p. 274.

47. A.J. Bird, 'John Speed's View of the Urban Hierarchy in Wales in the early Seventeenth Century', *Studia Celtica*, 10–11 (1975–6), 401–411.

48. Lobel, pp. 50–61.

49. W.L.D. Ravenhill, 'As to its Position in Respect to the Heavens', *Imago Mundi*, 28 (1976), 79–93.

50. M.J. Blakemore and J.B. Harley, 'Concepts in the History of Cartography . . . Questions of Definition' (1982) pp. 77–96.

51. See, for example, R.A. Skelton, *Decorative Printed Maps of the 15th to 18th Centuries* (London, 1952), p. 10.

52. J. Hall, *Dictionary of Subjects and Symbols in Art* (London, 1974) p. 139, under globe or orb, gives this general meaning of the symbol but it illustrates the danger of transferring general meanings into specific contexts to note that in Norden's day it had equally become a symbol associated with the person of Queen Elizabeth (see below).

53. G. Manley, 'Saxton's Survey of Northern England', *Geographical Journal* 83, (1934) 308–16.

54. See K. Clark, *Landscape into Art* (London, 1949), pp. 10–12; for the literary images see also M.H. Nicolson, *Mountain Gloom and Mountain Glory the development of the aesthetics of the infinite* (Ithaca, New York, 1959).

55. A.J. Bird (1975–6), p. 411, hints at another example: he notes the conventional signs on John Speed's county maps relating to Wales that 'The buildings, such as cathedral, church, priory, friary, college, castle, court, shire hall, and school, all represented spiritual and moral welfare, and law and order'.

56. Hall, p. 139.

57. E.L. Stevenson, *Terrestial and Celestial Globes. Their history and construction including a consideration of their value as aids in the study of geography and astronomy* (New Haven, 1921) 1, 179–83; 199–201.

58. M.F.S. Hervey, *Holbein's 'Ambassadors': The Picture and the Men; an historical study* (London, 1900) pp. 209–18. For fuller details of the use of globes and some of their contexts in Tudor England see H.M. Wallis, 'The First English Globe: a Recent Discovery' *Geographical Journal*, 117 (1951) 275–90 and H.M. Wallis, 'Further Light on the Molyneux Globes', *Geographical Journal* 121 (1955), 304–311.

59. See F.A. Yates, *The Art of Memory* (London, 1966) for the role of images in memory treatises. There is much in this book which is germane to an understanding of the functioning of cartographic language on a symbolic plane in Renaissance England. Sixteenth-century maps of Hell and Paradise were drawn to function as artificial memory for those concepts. See Plates 7a and 7b facing p. 128.

60. Strong, *passim*.

61. F.A. Yates, *Astraea: The Imperial Theme in the Sixteenth Century* (London, 1975), pp. 29–87.

62. H.M. Wallis, 'Globes in England up to 1660', *Geographical Magazine*, 35 (1962), 267–79, for reproductions and discussion of their role.

63. Strong, p. 131, showing Sir Henry Lee's portrait with this motif on his tunic.

64. Empire is for example explicit when Marlowe makes his dying Tamburlaine demand a map that he might
    '. . . see how much
    Is left for me to conquer all the world.'
    Quoted by A.F. Pollard, 'The Elizabethans and the Empire', *Proceedings of the British Academy*, 10 (1921), 1–20. See also E. Seaton, 'Marlowe's Map' in *Essays and Studies by Members of The English Association*, edited by E.K. Chambers (Oxford, 1924) 10, 13–35.

65. See R.W. Shirley, *Early Printed Maps of the British Isles A Bibliography 1477–1650* (London, 1980), for the carto-bibliographical evidence for the relatively rapid multiplication of the 'national' image; over 700 distinct maps have been identified for this period and, if there is added to this total some estimate of print runs and of the multiple use of individual maps, then a large number of Englishmen must have looked at a map of their country by the mid-seventeenth century.

66. Strong, p. 154. Queen Elizabeth embracing the Universe, in *Sphaera Civitatis*, by John Case, 1588, provides a similar example of the use of a cosmological diagram as a symbol of her terrestrial empire and of her spiritual mission on earth: see also H.M. Wallis (1962) p. 276. A similar discussion of imperial symbolism appears in H.M. Wallis, 'The Use of Terrestrial and Celestial Globes in England', *Actes du XIᵉ Congres International d'Histoire des Sciences.* (Wroclaw, 1968), pp. 204–12.

67. M.F.S. Hervey (1900) pp. 209–10. On religious and other symbolism in the celestial cartography of the Renaissance see D.J. Warner, *The Sky Explored: Celestial Cartography 1500–1800* (New York, 1979), pp. xi–xiii.

68. See B. Capp, *Astrology and the Popular Press. English Almanacs 1500–1800* (London, 1979) pp. 15–22, for an exploration of this relationship with implications for the meaning of celestial cartography in the period. There were, however, few terrestrial maps in the English almanacs although in the second half of the seventeenth century White's almanac provided its readers each year with a crude map of England, showing the county boundaries (Capp, p. 203).

69. For other evidence that maps and other types of celestial diagrams, as well as the applied sciences upon which they depended, sometimes conveyed meanings other than the literal see K. Thomas, *Religion and the Decline of Magic: Studies in popular beliefs in sixteenth- and seventeenth-century England* (London, 1971), especially Chapter 10 'Astrology: its practice and extent' and Chapter 11 'Astrology: its social and intellectual role'. One of the four main branches of judicial astrology during the sixteenth and seventeenth century was that of the *nativities*, maps of the sky made at the moment of a person's birth, either made on the spot at the request of the infant's parents, or reconstructed for individuals of mature years who could supply the details of their time and birth. It is certain that the meaning of these maps spilled over into celestial cartography in general during this period. For a summary of the wider context see also T.S. Pattie, *Astrology as Illustrated in the Collections of the British Library and the British Museum* (London, 1980).

70. T.D. Kendrick, *British Antiquity* (London, 1950), plate VII.

71. R. Strong, *The Renaissance Garden in England* (London, 1979) pp. 120–22; it is possible that this motif was associated with the myth of Elizabeth already referred to.

72. J. Bord, *Mazes and Labyrinths of the World* (London, 1976), pp. 114–15 reproduces examples from Thomas Hyll, *The Profitable Art of Gardening* (London, 1579). The standard work is still W.H. Matthews, *Mazes and Labyrinths. Their History and Development* (London, 1922). It may also be noted that a plan is the only way a maze can be meaningfully represented.

73. W.F. Jackson Knight, *Cumaean Gates. A reference of the sixth Aeneid to the initiation pattern.* (Oxford, 1936) pp. 54–55; 106; 124–5.

74. J. Speed, *A Prospect of the Most Famovs Parts of the World* (London, 1646), p. 4 writes 'the state of every kingdom well managed by prudent government, seems to me to represent a humane body, guided by the Soveraigntie of the Reasonable Soule'. The map thus represented a view of the 'outward Body & Lineaments of the now-flourishing British monarchy' and the 'Members, Veines, and Joynts' corresponded to the 'Shires, Rivers, Cities, and Townes'. For a wider discussion of macrocosmic/microcosmic philosophy in the Renaissance see E. Cassirer, *The Individual and the Cosmos in Renaissance Philosophy* (Oxford, 1963); pp. 109–12; S.K. Heninger Jr, *passim*.

75. T. Hawkes, p. 83; for a discussion of the application of linguistic structure in the study of historical evidence, including maps, see J.B. Harley, 'Historical Geography and its Evidence: reflections

on modelling sources', in *Period and Place. Research Methods in Historical Geography* edited by A.R.H. Baker and M. Billinge (Cambridge, 1982), pp. 261–73.

76. M.J. Blakemore and J.B. Harley, 'Concepts in the History of Cartography . . . Questions of Definition' (1982), pp. 77–96 for a discussion of this point.

77. See J.S. Keates, *Understanding Maps* (London, 1982), pp. 109–110, for the semantic problems which arise with this terminology.

78. E.M.J. Campbell, 'The Beginnings of the Characteristic Sheet to English Maps', *Geographical Journal*, 128 (1962), 411–15. It could be argued that they were merely copying a continental fashion but this seems the less likely explanation.

79. William Folkingham, *Feudigraphia: the Synopsis or Epitome of Surveying Methodized* (London, 1610), pp. 56–58 and other contemporary advice relevant to map colouring is summarised by W.L.D. Ravenhill, *John Norden's Manuscript Maps of Cornwall and its Nine Hundreds* (Exeter, 1972), pp. 34–8. William Leybourn, *The Compleat Surveyor: containing the whole art of surveying of land* (London, 1653), however, begins with an illustration of the depiction of hills to offer indirect advice on conventional signs in addition to colouring.

80. Cesare Ripa, *Iconologia*, (Padova, 1593; fascimile reprint of the third edition, 1603, New York, 1970).

81. E. Lynam, *The Mapmaker's Art. Essays on the history of maps* (London, 1953) p. 95.

82. R.A. Skelton, *Decorative Printed Maps*, p. 1; also 'Decoration and Design in Maps before 1700', *Graphis*, 7 (1951) 400–13.

83. E.H. Gombrich, *The Sense of Order. A study in the psychology of decorative art* (Oxford, 1979), p. 217.

84. T. Munro, *Form and Style in the Arts: an introduction to aesthetic morphology* (Cleveland, Ohio, 1970) pp. 8–11. A similar case to that for decoration could perhaps be argued in relation to the 'style' of Tudor maps. Although style is something of a catch-all term, including the way topographical details are represented as well as calligraphy and decorative features, it can be accepted that it communicated something of the original meaning of maps as perceived by contemporaries. For potentially helpful analogies to the significance of style in literature see S. Chatman, 'The Semantics of Style' in *Structuralism: a Reader*, edited by M. Lane (London, 1970), pp. 124–44.

85. Usually quoted in this context are John Dee, *The Elements of Geometrie* (1570), preface; and Robert Burton, *Anatomy of Melancholy* (London, 1621).

86. E. Lynam, *British Maps and Map-Makers* (London, 1947), p. 20.

87. J. Speed, *The Theatre of the Empire of Great Britaine* (London, 1611), preface. For a much wider discussion of ethnocentrism in cartography see Yi-Fu Tuan, *Topophilia: A study of environmental perception, attitudes, and values* (Englewood Cliffs, New Jersey, 1974), pp. 30–44.

88. William Camden, *Britain, Or A Chorographicall Description of the most flourishing Kingdomes, England, Scotland, and Ireland* . . . (London, 1610); quoted by J.B. Black, *The Reign of Elizabeth, 1558–1603*, second edition (Oxford, 1959) p. 283.

89. See T.D. Kendrick (1950) for the connections of Speed with other Elizabethan antiquaries; see also Sharpe, *Sir Robert Cotton* (1979).

90. See R. Weiss, *The Renaissance Discovery of Classical Antiquity* (Oxford, 1969), for the wider context of this intellectual movement and with examples of its interest in topography and mapping, pp. 90–104; also P. Burke, *The Renaissance Sense of the Past* (London, 1969).

91. M. Aston, 'English Ruins and English History: the dissolution and the sense of the past', *Journal of the Warburg and Courtauld Institutes*, 36 (1973), 231–55.

92. Sharpe, pp. 233–43.

93. See M. Beresford, *History on the Ground. Six studies in maps and landscapes,* revised edition (London, 1971), for examples.

94. See R. Dennys, *Heraldry and the Heralds* (London, 1982), for a discussion of 'The language of heraldry' relevant to its use on maps.

95. That William Folkingham in his *Feudigraphia* (1610) pp. 56–58, should have specified the map-maker's opportunities for decorating estate plans, together with more technical information, suggests that it was regarded as an important part of the total image rather than either optional or just incidental: the passage is quoted by R.A. Skelton, *Decorative Printed Maps*, pp. 16–17.

96. Hawkes, p. 83.

97. E.H. Gombrich, 'The Evidence of Images', in *Interpretation Theory and Practice* edited by C.S. Singleton (Baltimore, 1969), p. 71; also E.H. Gombrich, *Art and Illusion. A study in the psychology of pictorial representation* (London, 1962) pp. 172–74, 194–98. For a more general but nonetheless helpful discussion see T. Munro, pp. 63–65.

98. R.A. Skelton, *County Atlases of the British Isles 1579–1850* (London, 1970), pp. 10–11. The difficulty of using such evidence as a guide to meaning is, however, revealed by the alternative interpretations which have been put forward: F.A. Yates (1975), p. 63, suggests the engraving conveys 'something of the atmosphere of mysterious prophecy surrounding the advent of the Virgo . . . in the right-hand corner a man gazes through a telescope at a sign in the starry heavens. Here we see a representation of Virgo-Elizabeth as a celestial portent whose advent has been mysteriously foretold'.

99, See M. Corbett and R. Lightbown, *The Comely Frontispiece. The emblematic title-page in England 1550–1660* (London, 1979), pp. 153–161 for a full exposition of the various motifs.

100. Like the maps in Speed's *Theatre* the meaning of the maps in *Poly-Olbion* is not fully revealed apart from the context of the poem they illustrated. The text is critically edited, with reproductions of the maps, in *Poly-Olbion by Michael Drayton* edited by J.W. Hebel (Oxford, 1933) 4.

101. See R.A. Skelton and J. Summerson, *A Description of Maps and Architectural Drawings in the Collection made by William Cecil first Baron Burghley now at Hatfield House* (Oxford, 1971), pp. 25–28, on Lord Burghley's use of maps.

102. V. Morgan, 'Lasting Image of the Elizabethan Era' (1980), p. 406. W.G. Hoskins, *Provincial England: Essays in Social and Economic History* (London, 1963), p. 211 had made a similar point when he wrote 'it is not until the last quarter of the sixteenth century that we find men becoming intensely conscious of belonging to a particular county' and places this trend partly on the availability of county maps. For some seventeenth century attitudes see A. Everitt, 'The County Community' in *The English Revolution 1600–1660* edited by E.W. Ives (London, 1968) pp. 48–63.

103. In fact a systematic study of 'carto-literacy' in early modern England is required along the lines of D. Cressy, *Literacy and the social order. Reading and writing in Tudor and Stuart England* (Cambridge, 1980); while the materials are more fragmentary much material has already been assembled especially in the writings of E.G.R. Taylor.

104. J. Berger, *Ways of Seeing* (London, 1972).

105. R. Rees pp. 61–63; 71; J.A. Pinto, 'Origins and Development of the Ichnographic City Plan', *Journal of the Society of Architectural Historians*, 35 (1976), 35–50, suggests, incorrectly if the arguments in this paper are accepted, that the new measured town plans of Renaissance Europe were 'ill-suited to expressing symbolic values' and thus they 'constituted a new conceptual attitude toward the representation of cities, in which quantitative topographical relationships were given visual priority over . . . symbolic values'. See also J.G. Links, p. 82.

106. W.M. Ivins Jr, *Prints and Visual Communication* (Cambridge, Massachusetts, 1953), pp. 2–3. For the fuller implications of this for cartography see E.L. Eisenstein, *The Printing Press as an Agent of Change: Communications and cultural transformations in early-modern Europe*, 2 vols. (Cambridge, 1979).

Victor Morgan

The literary image of globes and maps in early modern England

On an earlier occasion I have considered some of the evidence for the use of Christopher Saxton's maps as a visual decorative motif.[1] In this paper I would like to adopt a somewhat different approach to maps-in-society by presenting the preliminary results of an investigation into the literary uses of globes and maps as images or metaphors. This investigation may provide some index of the degree of familiarity and sophistication in handling maps that authors assumed amongst their audience or readers.

It is arguable that to use maps as an image in literary works must depend on a prior familiarity with real maps and, to some degree, their practical uses, in order to make the cartographic image available in the literary context. This is not to deny that for some at least of the audience for literary works these allusions would be one of the indirect means by which they became familiar with maps, the occasions on which maps might be used, and what they might display. Most important of all, literary references are likely both to have reflected and reinforced the *values* – practical and abstract – that were associated with maps. Finally, it is in these literary allusions that we may hope to find any evidence for the degree to which in the contemporary mind maps were assimilated to other available visual images, and accommodated or undermined a pre-existent view of the ordering of the mental no less than the physical world. The examples and the comments that follow are based on a fairly promiscuous general reading in the period between 1520 and 1690, and on a more systematic examination of the writings of three authors in the Elizabethan and Jacobean periods: Edmund Spenser, William Shakespeare and John Donne.

The first conclusion to be drawn from this cursory survey is that by the late sixteenth century these authors assumed a familiarity with maps and globes amongst their various types of audience. Donne is clearly referring to the armchair geography espoused by men such as Robert Burton when he writes

Let sea-discoverers to new worlds have gone,
Let maps to others, worlds on worlds have shown[2]

and he is clearly indulging a typical conceit when he shrinks the real world to the summary of it provided by the characteristic markings of a terrestial globe,

All the globe's frame, and sphere's, is nothing else
But the meridians crossing parallels[3]

It could be argued that Donne's esoteric poetry, originally only circulated in manuscript and read by cultivated cognoscenti, could presume a knowledgeability not to be found elsewhere.[4] But this presumption is not supported by the use that Shakespeare makes of the image of the terrestial globe in some of his low or comedy scenes.

Prince Hal in *Henry IV, pt. ii* apostrophises Falstaff,

Why, thou globe of sinful continents, what a life dost thou lead![5]

While in *The Comedy of Errors* there is a more developed exploitation of the parallel image of rotundity of the earth and of the person. Dromio is bemoaning to his master, Antipholus, the disconcerting attentions paid to him by Nell, the kitchen maid:

ANT: Then she bears some breadth?
DRO: No longer from head to foot than from hip to hip: she is spherical like a globe; I could find out countries in her.
ANT: In what part of her body stands Ireland?
DRO: Marry, sir, in her buttocks; I found it out by the bogs.
ANT: Where Scotland?
DRO: I found it by the barrenness, hard in the palm of the hand . . .
ANT: Where America, the Indies?
DRO: O, sir, upon her nose, all o'er embellished with rubies, carbuncles, saphires, declining their rich aspect to the hot breath of Spain; who sent whole armadoes of caracks to be ballast at her nose.
ANT: Where stood Belgia, the Netherlands?
DRO: O, sir, I did not look so low . . .[6]

The experience of London life may have made both authors and possibly audience familiar not only with maps and globes, but also with their making. Donne wrote of how

On a round ball
A workman that hath copies by, can lay
An Europe, Afric, and an Asia,
And quickly makes that, which was nothing all[7]

An important point to note at this juncture is that in these contemporary literary usages it is the globe as much as the map that proffers itself for metaphorical exploitation.[8] This is because, as far as I can determine, the word 'globe' originally pertained to a physical shape, and only subsequently became a convenient shorthand for the terrestrial globe. With this prior and broader range of reference, images of the terrestrial globe could the more readily be assimilated to metaphor and imagery.

The Booke of prittie Conceites of 1586 recommends its readers to 'Go to a Glass-House or Glass-shop, & let them blow you a thin round Globe-glass, bigger than a penny Loaf . . .'[9] Here, it is the spherical nature of the object that is intended to be conveyed. In *Colin Clout's Come Home Again*, Spenser conjures up the image of rising clouds of smoke:

Her thoughts are like the fume of frankincense,
Which from a golden censer forth doth rise,
And throwing forth sweet odours mounts fro thence
In rolling globes up to the vaulted skies[10]

While in the *Faerie Queene* it is something like a fortune-tellers ball that seems to be intended:

Such was the glassy globe that Merlin made,
And gave unto King Ryence for his gard

. . .

           that mirrhour fayre[11]

Because the earth and moon were conceived of as spherical bodies, they also came to be referred to as globes. William Fulke in *A Goodly Gallerye with a most Pleasant Prospect into the Garden of Naturall Contemplation*, originally published in 1563, wrote that 'within the globe of the earth, be wonderful great holes, caves, or dungeons . . .' Elsewhere, he writes, 'Of Shields Globes or Bowles these Meteores also have their name of their fashion [*ie* depending on their apparent shape], because they are broad and appeare to be rounde . . .'[12] However, Fulke's grasp of the celestial realm was not unremittingly modern. In yet another place, writing of the appearance of the heavens he cited the argument of the philosopher Theophrastus that what men viewed in the sky was the interior of two concave spheres, and that 'it was the ioyning together or seeme of the two halfe globes, whiche made it ppeare more light in that place then in other'.[13]

In *Henry VI pt. ii,* Shakespeare uses the word 'globe' to mean this planet when he has the Queen implore Suffolk:

To France, sweet Suffolk. Let me hear from thee;
For whereso'er thou art in this world's globe
I'll have an Iris that shall find thee out'[14]

Again, in *Lear*, the Duke of Kent addresses the King:

Good King, that must approve the comman saw,
Thau out of heaven's benediction com'st
To the warm sun!
Approach, thou beacon to this under globe,
That by thy comfortable beams I may
Peruse this letter . . .

– here, 'globe' is used in the sense of the earth.[15]

A similar usage is also to be found in *Othello*, where the enormity of his murder of Desdemona makes Othello fear a comparable disruption in the realm of nature:

. . . O insupportable! O heavy hour!
Methinks it should be now a huge eclipse
Of sun and moon, and that th'affrighted globe
Did yawn at alteration[16]

Clearly, the idea of the earth as a shuddering globe is a potentially powerful image, and it is also used by Spenser:

Such was this Gyaunts fall, that seemd to shake
The stedfast globe of earth, as it for feare did quake[17]

In the poem, *The Rape of Lucrece,* Shakespeare directly exploits the conjoined notion of spherical shape conveyed by the word 'globe', and the sense that this is the shape of the world:

Her breasts, like ivory globes circled with blue,
A pair of maiden worlds unconquered,

. . .

These worlds in Tarquin new ambition bred[18]

Thus far, I have cited examples that suggest that the sense of spherical shape is associated, and perhaps increasingly associated, in the contemporary mind with the perception of 'the earth' or 'the world' as a sphere. But there is also evidence to suggest that the very existence of terrestrial globes may have aided this perception of the earth as a sphere. When in his famous speech on order in *Troilus and Cressida*, Ulysses suggests that

. . . the bounded waters
Should lift their bosoms higher than the shores,
And make a sop of all this solid globe[19]

it is in the context of preceding lines that allude to the order to be found in the heavens and its effect upon the earth. Surely this usage must depend for its effect on conjuring up a visual image that can relate the predominance of sea shown on a terrestrial globe to the land forms that they encompass? Again, Oberon's lines in *A Midsummer Night's Dream* may owe something to the notion of being able to encompass the representation of the real world in its image as a terrestrial globe:

We the globe can compass soon,
Swifter than the wand'ring moon[20]

In other instances the formulation clearly implies a knowledge of terrestrial globes, and uses this knowledge to draw comparison, or to elucidate other points. In his poem *Endimion and Phoebe*, Michael Drayton describes how

Shee in a fiery Mantle doth him wrap,
And carries him up from this lumpish mould,
Into the skyes, whereas he might behold,
The earth in perfect roundnes of a ball
Exceeding globes most artificiall! . . .[21]

Edmund Bolton in his *Armories*, explains the meaning of the words 'Convex' and 'Convexity', by means of an example. It is, he says, 'the outside of an hollow body, as concavity the inside. In a painted Globe of the world the descriptions are upon the convexitie thereof . . .[22]

In addition to this rather convoluted argument that has had to be pursued with regard to globes, it is also possible to argue from these literary sources for a familiarity with maps, and for the influence of maps in providing mental images.

Donne writes of 'plain maps', by which he means 'flat maps', a term he also uses,[23] and both Spenser and Shakespeare allude to maps in ways which suggest the contexts in which, in practical terms, contemporaries expected them to be found.

First, there are references to maps and charts as aids to travel and navigation. No doubt the experience of passages across the Irish sea inspired two of Spenser's similes that refer to the 'card and compas'.

As Pilot well expert in perilous wave,
That to a steadfast starre his course hath bent,
When foggy mistes or cloudy tempests have
The faithful light of that faire lampe yblent,

And cover'd heaven with hideous dreriment,
Upon his card and compas firmes his eye,
The maysters of his long experiment,
And to them does the steddy helme apply,
Bidding his winged vessell fairely forward fly[24]

In a second passage Spenser refers to the disregard for such aids to travel as a means of magnifying the daring of the militaristic Lady Britomart.[25] Again, in another instance, the lack of a 'card' is used as a means to indicate something unusual.[26] In *Cymbeline* there is a passage which suggests that 'to map' is being used as an analogue or metaphor for a verbal plan or description. Cloten enters and soliloquises near the cave of Belarius, in Wales:

I am near to th'place where they should meet, if Pisanio have mapp'd it truly . . . This is the very description of their meeting-place; . . .[27]

In *Titus Andronicus*, first performed and published in 1594, one of the characters, Tamora, Queen of the Goths, speaks in the character of Revenge. Titus seeks assurance that she is that abstraction, and alludes to the image of Hyperion's chariot crossing the heavens.

Now give some surance that thou art Revenge –
Stab them, or tear them on thy chariot wheels;
And then I'll come and be thy waggoner
And whirl along with thee about the globes,
Provide thee two proper palfreys, black as jet,
To hale thy vengeful waggon swift away . . .[28]

Now here 'waggoner' refers to the Hyperion image, but in this specific context it also means 'guide'. Either consciously or not, did Shakespeare also have in mind the navigational aid provided by Lucas Wagenaer's *Spieghel*, which first appeared in Dutch in 1585, and was printed in English as the *Mariners Mirrour* in 1588?[29] The allusion to 'globes' in the following line suggests that Shakespeare may have had a matrix of cartographic allusion in his mind when he composed this passage. Certainly in the opening scene of the *Merchant of Venice*, probably written about 1596, maps are specifically associated with foreign trade. Solanio addresses Antonio:

Believe me, sir, had I such venture forth,
The better part of my affections would
Be with my hopes abroad. I should be still
Plucking the grass to know where sits the wind,
Peering in maps for ports, and piers, and roads; . . .[30]

The second major context in which maps are presented in Shakespeare's plays is military. Sometimes the undiscerning interpretation of maps is used to characterise military men, as in the person of the professional Welshman, Fluellen, in *Henry V*,[31] or in Ulysses' complaint of the abuse directed at him by his allies:

They tax our policy and call it cowardice,
Count wisdom as no member of the war,
Forestall prescience, and esteem no act
But that of hand . . .
Why, this has not a finger's dignity:
They call this bed-work, mapp'ry, closet-war[32]

Here, the use of maps is clearly associated with the new techniques of warfare.

On other occasions, the military use of maps merges with the third context in which they are presented: the governmental.

In Act 3 of *Henry IV pt. i,* there is a council of war in which Hotspur, Worcester, Mortimer and Glendower divide up the Kingdom. The scene opens with some stage business clearly intended to acquaint the audience with a stage prop in the form of a map. Hotspur is introducing everyone to everyone else when he ejaculates '. . . a plague upon it! I have forgot the map', but Glendower responds 'No, here it is', thus effectively introducing it to the audience. Some seventy lines on, the map becomes the focus for their plans:

GLENDOWER: Come, here is the map;
shall we divide our right
According to our threefold order ta'en?
MORT: The Archdeacon hath divided it
Into three limits very equally:
England, from Trent and Severn hitherto,
By south and east is to my part assign'd;
All westward, Wales beyond the Severn shore,
And all the fertile land within that bound,
To Owen Glendower; and, dear coz, to you
The remnant northward lying off from Trent[33]

Henry IV pt. i was first produced in or about 1597. *King Lear* was first acted some nine years later, in 1606, and, of course, in the first scene the ageing King divides his Kingdom in three, again using a map for the purpose.[34]

The fourth context in which maps occur is that of the discoveries and the exotic. We have already noted Donne's allusion:

Let sea-discoverers to new worlds have gone,
Let maps to others, worlds on worlds have shown[35]

– a reference that suggests that when, in *To his Mistress Going to Bed,* he apostrophises her as 'America', it is because she reminds him of exploration and cartography:

   Licence my roving hands, and let them go
Before, behind, between, above, below.
O my America, my new found land,
My kingdom, safeliest when with one man manned,
My mine of precious stones, my empery,
How blessed am I in this discovering thee[36]

A similar association in Donne's mind of the metaphor of maps with the exotic is to be found in his 4th Satire, written around 1597. In this, he complains of the frustrations of waiting at Court:

   . . . but I have been in
A purgatory, such as feared hell is
A recreation, and scant map of this
. . .
Therefore I suffered this; towards me did run
A thing more strange than on Nile's slime the sun
E'er bred, or all which into Noah's Ark came:

A thing, which would have posed Adam to name:
Stranger than seven antiquaries' studies,
Than Afric's monsters, Guiana's rarities,
Stranger than strangers; . . .
[= a Courtier][37]

Shakespeare employs a similar image of exoticism, previously quoted, in the analogy of the globe presented by the rotund Nell in the *Comedy of Errors*, acted in 1594, and perhaps as early as 1592.[38]

If these are some of the practical contexts in which globes and maps are presented as familiar artifacts and images, is there any futher evidence that contemporaries understood that to which they alluded? Well, there is some suggestion that a proportion of users recognised that particular projections and conventions on maps were presenting them with the syntax and vocabulary of a language of signs. Indeed, this is what one would expect in an age familiar with the now arcane significations of the emblemata.

Thus, in *Upon the Annunciation and Passion falling upon one day 1608*, Donne wrote:

Tamely frail body abstain today; today
My soul eats twice, Christ hither and away.
She sees him man, so like God made in this,
That of them both a circle emblem is,
Whose first and last concur . . .

Where, of course, the circle is the circle of Christ's Annunciation and Passion coinciding, but also the traditional use of the circle as the emblem of God as perfection and infinity. But a few lines further on in the same poem he writes,

. . . this day hath shown,
Th'abridgement of Christ's story, which makes one
(As in plain maps, the furthest west is east)
Of the angels *Ave,* and *Consummatum est*[39]

– a paradoxical conceit that wholly depends on a grasp of the nature of the conventions implicit in flat maps. It is precisely the same image that he employs in *Hymn to God my God, in my Sickness*;

Whilst my physicians by their love are grown
Cosmographers, and I their map, who lie
Flat on this bed that by them may be shown
That this is my south-west discovery
Per factum tebris, by these straits to die
I joy, that in these straits, I see my west;
For, though their currents yield return to none,
What shall my west hurt me? As west and east
In all flat maps (and I am one) are one,
So death doth touch the resurrection[40]

Elsewhere Donne writes of the globe in the context of microcosms, of 'images' and 'pictures'.[41] However, Shakespeare is able to extract humour from the misinterpretation of the 'figures' or 'images' to be found in maps.

In *Henry V*, Fluellen compares the life of Alexander to that of the young Henry. 'I speak but in the figures and comparisons of it' as he says, and in the expectation that 'If you mark Alexander's life well, Harry of Monmouth's life is come after it indifferent well – for there is figures in all things'. But this type of interpretation of world history also leads him to a misinterpretation of the information provided on world maps, for he had previously conjectured:

I think it is in Macedon where Alexander is porn. I tell you, Captain, if you look in the maps of the 'orld, I warrant you sall find, in the comparisons between Macedon and Monmouth, that the situation, look you, is both alike. There is a river in Macedon; and there is also moreover a river at Monmouth; it is called Wye at Monmouth, but it is out of my prains what is the name of the other river; but 'tis all one, 'tis alike as my fingers is to my fingers, and there is salmons in both . . .[42]

Here, a character is presented as confusing the conventional signs for rivers, possibly for relief – 'the situations, look you, is both alike' – and possibly for decorative flourishes – 'there is salmons in both'. The same signs signify the same things but different places: our two hands are separate hands. But, of course, the humour of the situation depends on the audience, or at least a proportion of the audience, recognising Fluellen's error in confusing the argument from literary figures or significations, with the figures and significations of cartography.

But Shakespeare also exploited the notion of the map as a microcosm that signified a larger matter, or fundamentals of character. In *The Rape of Lucrece* he develops the concept that sleep is a model or analogue of death. He describes Lucrece,

Her eyes like marigolds, had sheath'd their light,
And canopied in darkness sweetly lay,
Till they might open to adorn the day.
Her hair like golden threads, play'd with her breath –
O modest wantons! wanton modesty! –
Showing life's triumph in the map of death,
And death's dim look in life's mortality[43]

Here, sleep is a sign, a microcosm, which is a map, of the larger matter, death.

I have already cited a number of instances in which the human body or the human face is treated as a metaphor for maps, or vice versa. This process was encouraged by two conditions. The first was the extent to which the body, or a part of the body, the face, was round, or circular, and thus approximated to a globe, or the circular representations of the two hemispheres of certain maps. The second was the familiar theory of the microcosmos and the macrocosmos, to which I have already alluded in passing, and in which the body of man was a recension of the larger universe.[44] Closely associated with this was the theory of the humours, which lay behind the literary theory of the theophrastian character which was enjoying a revival in the late sixteenth century and early seventeenth century.[45] In this context the face was the microcosm of the person, and showed forth the dominant traits of personality, just as a map is the microcosm of a place, and conveys by signs the characteristics of the real place it epitomises. Thus, in *Coriolanus*, the testy Menenius Agrippa confronts the two tribunes of the people:

I am known to be a humorous patrician, and one that loves a cup of hot wine with not a drop of allaying Tiber in't, said to be . . . hasty and tinder-like upon too trivial motion; one that converses more with the buttock of the night than with the forehead of the morning. What I think I utter, and spend my malice in my breath . . . if the drink you give me touch my palate adversely, I make a crooked face at it . . . and though I must be content to bear with those that say you are reverend grave men, yet they lie deadly that tell you you have good faces. If you see this in the map of my microcosm [ie face], follows it that I am known well enough too? What harm can your bisson conspectuities glean out of this character, if I be known well enough too?[46]

The dominant character or humour is supposed to be manifest in the face, the microcosm and map of the person, just as in *Henry VI pt. ii*, the King addresses his uncle, Humphrey, Duke of Gloucester,

. . . in thy face I see
The map of honour, truth, and loyalty[47]

and in *The Rape of Lucrece* it is

The face, that map which deep impression bears
Of hard misfortune, carv'd in it with tears[48]

while sonnet 68 both depends on familiarity with maps as a graphic form and exploits the metaphor of the face as a map. Through these devices, it proffers the microcosm of the aged person and his face, as an exemplification of certain good. Thus the metaphor of maps, and possibly through the metaphor, maps themselves, become imbued with personality and acquire a moral role.

Thus is his cheek the map of days outworn,
When beauty liv'd and died as flowers do now,
Before these bastard signs of fair were born
Or durst inhabit on a living brow;
Before the golden tresses of the dead,
The right of sepulchres, were shorn away
To live a second life on second head,
Ere beauty's dead fleece made another gay.
In him those holy antique hours are seen,
Without all ornament, itself and true,
Making no summer of another's green,
Robbing no old to dress his beauty new;
   And him as for a map doth Nature store,
   To show false Art what beauty was of yore[49]

For Sir Richard Baker, writing in defence of the stage in the 1630s, there were parallels between maps and plays as microcosms. He asked his reader to 'be content, as to see the wide world drawn in a map, and a large history in an abridgement; so to see, and favour plays, which are nothing, but epitomes of the world's behaviour'.[50] This paralleling of maps and the theatre is interesting in itself, but also because it points in a further direction. For although the image of the globe does not seem to have carried the same moral freightage as that loaded on to maps, it too was eminently suited to incorporation into the prevailing ideas of the macrocosmos and the microcosmos. For, of course, many of the Shakespearian plays from which I have quoted were performed at the theatre in Southwark called *The Globe* where Prospero spoke of:

. . . the baseless fabric of this vision,
The cloud-capp'd towers, the gorgeous palaces,
The solemn temples, the great globe itself,
Yea, all which it inherit, shall dissolve,
And, like this insubstantial pageant faded,
Leave not a rack behind . . .[51]

Here, the globe is the world, but it is also the theatre, and an appropriately named theatre, given the beliefs of the time, for its plays are, in Baker's words 'epitomes of the world's behaviour'. But perhaps it was also named with terrestrial globes in mind, for as we have seen, they too were acknowledged as microcosms or epitomes.

More could be said of the use of the literary image of maps and globes as microcosms. But perhaps enough evidence has been cited to make it evident that we are confronted with a paradox. In an earlier paper I suggested that in the late sixteenth-century maps were adopted as visual decorative motifs by a sophisticated society familiar with the use of visual signs and symbols.[52] The literary evidence indicates that, through the use of simile and metaphor, maps and globes were accommodated to a pre-existent world view of the relationship between the macrocosmos and the microcosmos. Moreover, these metaphorical usages of the image of map or globe, may have had implications for the attitudes adopted towards *real* maps and globes, encouraging characterisation, personification, and the association with them of the values attached to the use of their image in literature.

Maps and globes were the products of a number of new technologies. They are often cited as evidence for the discovery of new physical worlds on the earth and in the sky, and employed as an index of a changing perception of the mental world. Yet the evidence suggests that as a literary image they could as well be used to re-invigorate an existing world view, and to reinforce traditional values.

More certainly, we may conclude that in order to have worked satisfactorily in the literary contexts, both general and specific, in which they were employed, what may be described as practical allusions to real maps must have both *reflected* and *reinforced* an existing familiarity with maps and their various uses.

The evidence also suggests the recognition of maps as a language of signs. In the works of literary men, no sharp demarcation was made between this class of signs and those to be found in the parallels of history, the metaphors of language and the visual emblemata so popular in the period.

1. Victor Morgan, 'The Cartographic Image of "the Country" in Early Modern England', *Transactions of the Royal Historical Society*, 5 ser., 29 (1979), 129–154, and 'Lasting Image of the Elizabethan Era', *Geographical Magazine*, 52 (1980), 401–498.
2. John Donne, *The Good Morrow*, 11.12–13 (p. 60). References to Donne are taken from *John Donne: The Complete English Poems*, edited by A.J. Smith, Penguin Books, 1971). For Burton's armchair geography, see Robert Burton, *The Anatomy of Melancholy* (1621; London, Everymans Library, 1964) II, 89, I, 18.
3. *The Cross* 11.23–4 (p. 326), and in Maria's description of Malvolio's face; 'He does smile his face into more lines than is in the new map with the augmentation of the Indies' (*Twelfth Night*, III. 2. 74–76, p. 364a. The edition used is, *William Shakespeare: The Complete Works*, edited by Peter Alexander, London, 1951).
4. John Buxton, *Elizabethan Taste* (London, 1963), pp. 317–338.
5. *Henry IV, pt. ii*, II, 4, 275–6 (p. 529a).
6. *The Comedy of Errors*, III, 2, 111–137 (p. 125a).
7. *A Valediction: of Weeping*, 11.10–13 (p. 89).
8. On the availability of globes see H.M. Wallis, 'The Use of Terrestrial and Celestial Globes in England', *Actes du XIᵉ Congres International d'Histoire des Sciences* (Warsaw, 1968) pp. 204–12, and R.M. Fisher, 'William Crashawe and the Middle Temple Globes 1605–15', *Geographical Journal*, 140 (1974), 105–12.
9. *The Booke of prittie conceites taken out of Latin, Italian, French, Dutch and Englishe*. (London, 1586?) Sig. A3.
10. Edmund Spenser, *Colin Clout's Come Home Again* (1591) in *The Shepherd's Calendar and Other Poems*, edited by Philip Henderson (London, Everyman's Library, 1956) p. 261.
11. Edmund Spenser, *The Faerie Queene*, III. 2. 21–22 edited by J.W. Hales. (London, Everyman's Library, 1910), I, pp. 357, 358). In context this appears to be an allusion to Walsingham's role as spy-master for Elizabeth.
12. William Fulke, *A Goodly Gallerye with a most Pleasant Prospect into the Garden of Naturall Contemplation* (1655 edn) III C. II; II, B.I.V. wing 2260A.
13. William Fulke, III, E. VI, V–VII.
14. *Henry VI, pt. ii*, III. 2. 405–407 (p. 647a).
15. *King Lear*, II, 2. 155–160 (p. 1087a).
16. *Othello*, V, 2. 101–104 (p. 1150b).
17. *The Faerie Queene*, I. 8. 23. (p. 109). A similar image is also implied by Shakespeare in *Troilus and Cressida*, I. 3. 85–6 (p. 793a).
18. *The Rape of Lucrece*, 11. 407–411 (p. 1289a). This image of the globe follows on closely one that refers to a map (1.402).
19. *Troilus and Cressida*, I. 3, 85–86 (p. 793a).
20. *A Midsummer Night's Dream*, IV. 1. 94–95 (p. 215b).
21. Michael Drayton, 'Endimion and Phoebe. Ideas Latmus' 11.664–669 in *The Works of Michael Drayton*, edited by J. William Hebel (Oxford, 1961) I, p. 146. Drayton's topographical and cartographic interests in another work – *Poly Olbion*, – are, of course, well-known.
22. Edmund Bolton, *The Elements of Armories* (London, 1610). DD. iiir
23. John Donne, *Upon the Annunciation and Passion falling upon one day. 1608* 1.21 (p. 329) and *Hymn to God my God, in my Sickness*, 11.7, 14 (pp. 347, 348).
24. *The Faerie Queen*, II. 7. 1 (p. 240).
25. *The Faerie Queene*, III. 2. 7. (p. 354).
26. *The Faerie Queene*, III. 8. 31. (p. 444).
27. *Cymbeline*, IV. 1. 1–30 (p. 1221b).
28. *Titue Andronicus*, V. 2. 46–51 (p. 896b).
29. D.W. Waters, *The Art of Navigation in England in Elizabethan and Early Stuart Times* (London 1958), pp. 168–175.
30. *The Merchant of Venice*, I. 1. 14–19 (p. 223a).
31. *Henry V*, IV. 7. 21–42 (p. 579a-b).
32. *Troilus and Cressida*, I. 3. 197–205. (p. 794a).
33. *Henry IV, pt. i*, III. 1. 5–79 (pp. 496a–497a).
34. *King Lear*, I. 1. 36–7 (p. 1073b).
35. John Donne, *The Good Morrow*, 11.12–13.
36. John Donne, *Elegy 19, To his Mistress Going to Bed*, 11.25–29 (p. 125).
37. John Donne, *Satire 4*, 11.2–3, 17–23 (p. 164). A similar association is to be found in *Hymn to God my God, in my Sickness*.
38. See above, note 6.
39. John Donne, *Upon the Annunciation and Passion falling upon one day. 1608*, 11.1–5, 19–22 (pp. 328, 329).
40. John Donne, *Hymn to God my God, in my Sickness*, 11.6–15 (pp. 347–8).
41. 'The Cross', 11.2, 7, 23–4 (p. 326).
42. *Henry V*, IV. 7. 22–33 (p. 579a).
43. *The Rape of Lucrece*, 11.397–403 (p. 1289a).
44. E.M.W. Tillyard, *The Elizabethan World Picture* (1943; London, Penguin Books edn, 1963) pp. 107–122.
45. Benjamin Boyce, *The Theophrastian Character in England to 1642* (Cambridge, Mass., 1947), and the introduction to *Samuel Butler 1612–1680: Characters*, edited by Charles W. Daves (London, 1970).
46. *Coriolanus*, II. 1. 43–60 (p. 837b).
47. *Henry VI, pt. ii*, III. 2. 202–3 (p. 640a).
48. *The Rape of Lucrece*, 11.1712–3 (p. 1305a). Malvolio's foolishness is manifest in his face (*Twelfth Night*, III, 75–77, p. 364b).
49. Sonnet 68 (p. 1319b).
50. Sir Richard Baker, *Theatrum Redivivum, or the Theatre Vindicated* (London, 1662). p. 141
51. *The Tempest*, IV. 1. 1551–57 (p. 21a).
52. Morgan, 'Cartographic Image'.

Marcus Merriman

Italian military engineers in Britain in the 1540s

In October 1548 an English prisoner of war, held in Edinburgh for over three months, finally raised his ransom and returned to Berwick, then, as now, part of England.[1] The man in question, Thomas Carlisle, had been captured during a confused sortie he had made with others from Haddington, at the time the most modern fortress existing in Britain. The English had built it as part of their attempt to force the Scots to agree to 'the golden and godly union' of the two realms by the marriage of Mary Queen of Scots to Edward VI: the war popularly known across the border as 'The Rough Wooing'.[2] It had been built to what is now generally called *trace italienne* design: thick earth walls, quadrilinear in overall layout with massive angle-bastions at the four corners which provided not only firepower outwards, but also flanking fire along the walls so that no blind spots existed, enabling the defenders comprehensively to rake every inch of ground about the place.[3] The French meanwhile had sent a professional army, containing numerous Italians, to aid the Scots in their resistance to the English attempt to force Anglo-Scottish union; in return Mary was to be married to a future king of France, with a subsequent Franco-Scottish union in view.

Much of Carlisle's report on his arrival at Berwick to Thomas Fisher actually concerned Leith, which the French were then in the process of transforming into one of the most modern *trace italienne* fortifications in Europe so as to counter Haddington.[4] But he also commented that the French had at their first coming to Scotland 'devised a traves walle betwene the towne of Edenbrugh and the castell'. This wall 'with a poynted bulwerk in the myddes' was in the summer of 1548 being constructed, and was by October already up to a man's height. What Carlisle described to Fisher – and he drew a 'grocely pricked out' line drawing of the wall (pl. 17) – must be the 'fort of the castle hill', also called 'the spur', which was to cause the English such trouble when they besieged Edinburgh Castle in 1573 (pl. 18).[5]

It is not clear just who was the 'engener' (Carlisle's term) the French employed, but a strong possibility is Migliorino Ubaldini who on 5 February 1548 had been given a patent by the governor of Scotland 'to perfect the Scots in the knowledge of arms and to organise the defence of the realm'.[6] Ubaldini remains an infuriatingly shadowy figure, although he did write to Mary of Guise, queen dowager of Scotland, in June 1548 requesting permission to tour the highlands ('ver li selvagi') and again in September to comment on the difficulties he was having both with the work after the departure of Pietro Strozzi, one of the most famous of all Italian soldiers in the sixteenth-century, and with the workforce at Dunbar, another notable French strength in Scotland.[7] Ubaldini may well be the 'Italiane devisar of the forte of the castell hill' mentioned in Scottish financial accounts for whose keep Patrick Barron's wife was paid £11 expenses in early March 1548.[8]

But Ubaldini was not the only Italian in Scotland at this time; the governor employed one called 'Theodorus' as secretary 'for writting of certane missiwis to the King of France and to syndry other gret men in thai partis';[9] moreover, a kinsman, Petruccio Ubaldini served with the English garrison at Haddington in 1549.[10] This Ubaldini, a Florentine, perhaps of protestant views, apparently stayed in England after the end of the 'Rough Wooing' in 1550 only until Mary's accession in 1553. He resided in Venice before returning to England during the more receptive climate of Elizabeth's reign.

During his long time in England he became something of a court favourite, wrote numerous poems and dedicated a number of works to prominent Elizabethan courtiers, in addition to preparing a report on the fate of Spanish Armada off the coast of Ireland. His *Descrittione del Regno di Scotia et delle Isole sue Adjacenti*, which was only published in Antwerp in 1588 had in fact been prepared, so he maintained in its original dedication of 1576 to Henry Fitzalan, Earl of Arundel, as early as 1550, just after his return from Scotland and indeed it was almost a verbatim translation of Hector Boethius's *Scotorum Historiae*, first published in 1526.[11] Ubaldini drew on his time in Scotland not only here, however, for in a *Relatione della Ingleterra* prepared in 1551, he mentioned Scotland a number of times and even Haddington, where he had served.[12]

This relative profusion of Ubaldinis, the one an engineer, the other a writer, serves to illustrate one theme which will be elaborated in this short essay: a lot of Italians were about in Britain in the 1540s, closely involved with the prosecution of a highly aggressive and very expensive war.

War can be, and often is, a 'school' in which men learn; let us speculate about this school of war. Italians, such as Leonardo da Vinci, were drawing city plans to scale as early as 1502–3, witness his map of Imola and other maps of the Tuscan war zone. Within the heritage of European cartography, then, scales are Italian in origin. Secondly, military engineers first and most widely employed scales.[13] Next, note that during the period 1539–50, there was a military building programme in England and the rest of Britain perhaps unsurpassed in cost and numbers of sites fortified until the nineteenth century. Moreover, increasingly during the late 1540s these fortifications were constructed to a type of design – the *trace italienne*.

Furthermore, not only were 'Italian' ideas current in Britain, but also Italians were active in the country, surveying sites, proposing how they should be made defensible and working with numerous English military engineers. It was, moreover, during this very time that English surveyors and map makers began extensively to employ scales on their maps. The conclusion seems inescapable that English surveyors learned how to apply scales from Italy, just as they learned so much else from the cradle of the Renaissance.

This 'conclusion' is however mere kite-flying; the evidence is suggestive, but the conclusion is not proven. The numerous obstacles to such an engaging interpretation can best be highlighted by the remarks of three historians of varying familiarity with the problems of interpreting the sixteenth century. Dean L.R. Shelby spent countless hours poring over the plans for a number of sites built on by English engineers in the 1540s in the course of his seminal study *John Rogers – Tudor Military Engineer*. In his work, he mentions numerous plans, or 'plats' as the Tudors termed them, of sites where Rogers worked. Every nuance of colouring, each squiggle of hand-writing was assessed and analysed to determine who actually executed this plethora of plats prepared for Henry VIII and the Duke of Somerset during Rogers's extraordinarily active career during which he clearly emerged, along with Richard Lee, as the foremost English designer of fortified places. But despite the mass of surviving evidence and despite Dean Shelby's consummate knowledge of the topic, he rarely, and usually only by inference, could ascribe certain plats to Rogers's hand. At Hull, where Rogers was the only surveyor of note, it is pretty certain he either executed or directed the preparation of the plans, many of which were drawn to a scale. But for an earlier period (Guines in 1541) and a later one (Boulogne in 1545–46) for which numerous plans were prepared to scale, Rogers's execution can be surmised but not conclusively proved.[14]

Secondly, as C.H. Carter reminds us from his wide familiarity with diplomatic correspondence, despite the staggering mass of drafts, copy books and original letters which do come down to us, 'there is obviously no greater "bias" in the "history" that remains available to us in the form of surviving evidence than the fact that some survives and some does not.'[15] Many plats obviously did not survive. To take but one example, when Protector Somerset had the French ambassador to dinner in June 1548, he proudly displayed 'le dessaing en plateforme' of Haddington which was just being built. That plat has vanished; so too has the one the ambassador had prepared which he sent to Henry II of France. Numerous other plans for Berwick, Boulogne, Dunbar, Edinburgh, Stirling, Dunglass and other sites in Britain were stated to have been prepared, but have since been lost, as a close reading of the fourth volume of *The History of the King's Works* amply demonstrates.

Moreover, it is notoriously difficult to substantiate how ideas, concepts and techniques were transmitted during a period such as the sixteenth century. Even in an area as strenuously studied and richly documented as the Reformation, G.R. Elton has had ruefully to concede about the flood of tracts which accompanied it that however much we can say about the propagandists who wrote them and however detailed an analysis can be made of the content of these polemics, when it comes to the impact such rhetoric had on men's minds, 'no very precise answer can be given.'[16] So, too, with map making: as P.D.A. Harvey has argued in his penetrating article on the Portsmouth map of 1545, it is next to impossible to prove how English mapmakers came to employ scales.[17]

The importance of his overall case needs reiteration. Something like 30 topographical maps which were executed in England between 1350 to 1500 survive today, but for the next half-century, 1500–50, the output apparently soared to a figure of perhaps 200. The vast majority of these were picture-maps, crude views from an elevation with a perspective.[18] An excellent example is the view of Newcastle-upon-Tyne, doubtless executed by Gian Tommaso Scala in 1545 when he was in the area working at Tynemouth (pl. 19). What we have here is a 'portrait' of the city, an impression of its landscape, street plan, houses clustered about, the walls and castle all drawn like a picture in perspective.[19] As a view, it is vigorous, colourful and holds many clues for the urban historian, but for those needing precise measurements, it is almost useless, being very much of the medieval school of pictorial representation of topography, where precision is conspicuous by its absence.

When measurement is even mentioned on these maps, it is usually just stated as on the plat of Castlemilk of 1547 (pl. 20) where distances were simply asserted: Castlemilk to Dumfries: 'ten mylis', with little correlation between that 'fact' and the fact of the piece of paper before the reader of the 'map'.[20] These were 'picture maps', with no implied or explicit attempt to draw to any consistent scale.

The Castlemilk 'platte' showed towns, fortresses in bird's-eye view surrounded by impressionistically painted hills: very much a medieval map in conception and reception.[21] But it clearly worked for the Protector of England, Somerset, for whom it was intended. These picture-maps (which are like nothing so much as the table placemats which American restaurant chains habitually design for their customers: Bicentennial America with little pictures of Mount Vernon, Liberty Hall, The Boston Tea Party or which British railways used to issue to their travellers: Crewe, York Minster, Edinburgh Castle) have had a long heritage and obviously correspond to a need for a general orientation. But they have little utility for anyone needing the precise orientation such as that given by Ordnance Survey coordinates.

Nonetheless, the sixteenth century was a time when scale maps were established. Professor Harvey estimates that for 1500–50, 40 maps were scale maps. Over the next half-century, the scale was to enter the minds of cartographers as the standard to which they must aspire and map readers as what they should expect. To appreciate just how radical an alteration was taking place, compare Scala's 1545 view of Newcastle (pl. 19) with the map of Portsmouth, executed in the same year, which Professor Harvey has called 'the earliest ichnographic map we have of any town in England' (pl. 21).[22]

Most of these 40 scale maps come from the 1540s; four of Guines in 1541 (perhaps even earlier: 1539), one of Calais in 1541, three of Hull executed in 1541–2; Dover, Harwich, Carlisle in the early 1540s; French territories in 1545–7; Scotland in 1547–50.[23] The now famous 1545 plan of Portsmouth, which Professors Biddle and Harvey have so intensively and skilfully studied, has a stated scale; one inch to one hundred feet (1:1200).[24] For Boulogne in 1546, numerous plats have scales: what Shelby calls 'Plat B of Ambleteuse' has: 'The Ynche conteyneth 200 fote' (1:2400); what he calls 'Survey II and III of Boulogne' has 'The Inche stondeth for 500 fete' (1:6000).[25] When the Earl of Rutland had prepared a set of plats of the fortresses in Scotland under his command in late 1549, a variety of scales were used: 'at 32 fotte to thinche' (1:384) for Fast Castle to '40 ffotte to the inche' (1:480) for Lauder to the more normal 'drawn at 60 fotte to thinche' (1:720) for Roxburgh and Eyemouth.[26]

The obvious question is, how did English surveyors come to employ scales? Given the impossibility of positively ascribing most plans to certain individuals, and given the selective survival of evidence, no very precise answer can be given. Let us just take one aspect of the problem. As Professor Harvey has argued, it would seem that (German possibilities aside) the obvious source, given da Vinci's work in Tuscany at the beginning of the century, is from Italy.[27] Certainly there were numerous Anglo-Italian contacts at this time. Englishmen travelled and worked in Italy; it was an Englishman (the perhaps fictitious Richard Wentworth) with whom Niccolo Tartaglia held his dialogues concerning mathematics and how to make scale maps in his *Quesiti e Inventioni Diverse* first published in Venice by 1538.[28] Italians also lived and worked in England, among them Girolamo da Treviso who entered Henry VIII's service also in 1538. Noted by Vasari as an 'engineer' for the king, he prepared at least one map of

Montreuil and seeing as he was at the siege of Boulogne, he may well have met English surveyors there, such as John Rogers and Richard Lee. A Sicilian Antonio 'Fagion' was paid for work on fortifications in March 1538; Archangelo Arcano, a gunfounder and engineer, was employed also from 1538; in April 1540 a 'Neopolitan' was paid for his proposals for a castle. A seventy-year-old Italian at Henry's court promised in 1541 to build some sort of telescope so the king could view Dieppe harbour from the top of Dover Castle. Giovanni di Rossetti, 'master of ordnance and engineer' to be widely employed (like Arcano) in the north during the 1540s, was in Henry's service by 1543.[29]

So far so good, but this does not really take us very far, being but a catalogue of contacts without proof that transmission of the mysteries of the scale took place at this time or by Anglo-Italian contact. Both Professors Harvey and Hale, profoundly knowledgeable about cartography on the one hand and Italian military engineers on the other, have searched in vain for a transmission-interchange point.[30] Indeed, such proof is probably, given the constraints outlined above, impossible. But a number of variables must also be kept in mind. It is not certain then any foreign 'source' must exist: the demands of the job of building castles and forts may simply have given rise to the application of scales without the need for foreign inspiration. Indeed, how *did* Italians come to apply them?

Scales did not sweep the board overnight: of the flood of maps between 1500–50, the majority were indeed *not* to scale and for a long time afterwards maps would include both scale-plan and perspective birds'-eye-view. The plat of Eyemouth, probably executed for the Duke of Rutland in 1549, showed the walls, ditch and flankers clearly drawn to precise dimensions (although indeed the Rutland plan does not correspond as much as one would like to a modern archaeological site survey); living quarters, storehouses and other ancillary buildings for the garrison were rendered in perspective.[31] This was also the case with many of Rogers's plats for the Boulonnais.[32] When, in 1560, the state of the siege of Leith was recorded on the day of the French surrender (7 July), although as precise a scale as one could ask for was given: 'The Scale of this Plat is eightye paces to ane ynche. Every pace conteyning 5 foote geometricall' or 1 inch to 400 feet (1:4800), both Leith and Edinburgh were rendered in elevation, as vigorously and assertively as Scala's 'portrait' of Newcastle fifteen years earlier.[33]

Moreover, by no means all Italians drew to scale, as will be evident later in this piece. But no single transmission point needs to be isolated: different Englishmen learned how to draw to scale plans in any number of different sorts of ways. Failure to pinpoint the first conversations, such as that suggested between Tartaglia and Wentworth, is thus perhaps not particularly important. What we can describe is a much more generalised phenomenon: the intercourse between Englishmen and Italians during which ideas about scales could have been mentioned, when previously received notions could have been reinforced and when the practical application of certain techniques may have lead to a more wide-spread application of this new approach to plat and map drawing.

Two points to appreciate are that during the 1540s something of a revolution was taking place in how English surveyors designed places of strength and defence and that these innovative concepts originated from Italy. But the process was gradual and England's need for more potent defence did not initally mean that the new Italianate concepts for fortification were employed. Rather, during the course of an intensive building programme, new approaches were introduced, often promoted by Italians, who in the course of their employment may well have also demonstrated the obvious efficacy of using precise measurements on plats and maps. Let us now examine that experience without expecting to find the precise moment when a scale was laid out for the first time before an Englishman, but rather a process by which English surveyors became familiar with Italian techniques.

There was indeed a lot of building for English engineers to survey, plan and execute during the 1540s, for in 1539 Henry VIII, fearful of a French and Imperial invasion, began a massive fortress-building programme from along the south coast to as far north as Berwick, Wark and Carlisle. These new places of strength and the adaptation of older castles were almost all executed to a design plan which Professor Hale has characterised as 'transitional'. Although 'massively beautiful machines designed for the maximum emission of balls and bullets', these masonry firepower edifices suffered from serious defects. They were expensive to build (an average of £6000 each) and took a long time to complete. Moreover, being rounded, they did not provide adequate flanking fire so that all parts of their walls could be defended; numerous blind spots existed which the defenders could not defend and this unflanked dead ground could be mined. Furthermore, at the very time they were being constructed, a new design idiom was being learned from Italy by the French and by other Europeans. This was the *trace italienne*, the nature of which has already been briefly described for Haddington. The point to appreciate is that these new *trace italienne* fortifications were completely self-sustained and independently defensible strengths with no blind spots or weakening 'dead ground'. Also important, when constructed primarily in earth, they could be erected by a relatively unskilled workforce very rapidly indeed and at very low cost; Haddington was made defensible against a Franco-Scottish siege force of perhaps 10,000 men in little over two months in 1548 and cost apparently no more than £1,423 to erect.[34]

The French first began to appreciate the virtues of this new method of fortification during the south of France and Piedmont campaigns of 1536. When Montmorency laid out a fortified camp near Avignon in July, he was advised by two Italians to build what appears to have been a forerunner of Haddington: ditch, rampart, flanking bastions and resulting platforms. At Fossano, Moncalieri, Savigliano, Carignano and Pinerolo, Italianate angle-bastions were employed. At Turin the French captured a fortress built to the new design by the Duke of Savoy in 1535; they then completed the ditches and faced the four famously large angle bastions in stone.[35] Turin became a yardstick by which commentators judged fortresses; Somerset told the French ambassador in May 1548 that Haddington was 'une des plus belles et fortes places après Thurin',[36] and Tartaglia's *Quesiti e Inventioni diverse* contained a plan of it.[37]

This 'school of war' in northern Italy was clearly a period when Montmorency and numerous other French commanders may first have come to appreciate the value of the new technique. Italian engineers and their ideas were quickly moved north by Francis I: Antonio da Castello was put to work in 1537 strengthening St Pol, Thérouanne, Hesdin, Montreuil and Boulogne. Girolamo Bellarmato of Siena enlarged Le Havre with an Italianate bastion in 1540; Girolamo Marini was employed at Landrecy and Luxembourg in 1543, then in the design for the fortification of the towns of Vitry-le-François and Villefranche-sur-Meuse.[38]

Turning to another 'school of war', Henry VIII's Boulogne campaign of 1543–46, we see yet another 'transmission chamber', as Professor Hale has termed it, for these new ideas. After the stunning capture of Boulogne in September 1544 by Henry VIII, Francis I began (as soon as the winter passed) to build counter-defences so as to hem the English into their new conquest, their new pale. The principal strength was a five-bastioned earth-built fort designed by Antonio Melloni called Fort d'Outreau.[39] It is interesting to note that when a plan of Henry's new possession was drawn (perhaps not by Rogers) in July 1545, the draughtsman did not quite know what to make of the five bastions (pl. 22). Instead of the straight angle of the bastion with its walls going back to the orillons, rather curious affairs, somewhat like the ace of spaces from a deck of cards was described.[40] But within a year, Rogers (in his second and third surveys of Boulogne) accurately described Fort d'Outreau (pl. 23) with a confidence arising from a sound knowledge of how a *trace italienne* fortress worked.[41] How did he gain this wisdom, which he and the English commanders in Boulogne (including the Earl of Hertford – to become Protector Somerset in 1547 – in addition to Lord Grey of Wilton, Sir Thomas Palmer and Lee, who were to execute Somerset's war policy in Scotland during 1547–49) so confidently executed when building their new defences for the pale: at Ambleteuse, in Boulogne itself and at Boulogneberg in 1546–7?[42] One way may well have been by just imitating Melloni's work on the other side of the river.

The loss of Boulogne was not immediately accepted by Francis and freed from a bruising war with the Emperor in 1544, he determined to make a massive assault on Henry VIII: this he would do by attacking Boulogne, sending a fleet against the south coast, likewise attacking by sea on the north-east coast and with an army from Scotland. These plans became quickly known to Henry and indeed most of the ventures (although unsuccessful) were attempted; in fact the great muster of the realm in 1545 was the most massive England was to experience until its next greatest crisis, the Armada of 1588.[43] The king naturally looked to the nation's defences and sought to plug gaps which had been missed in the great building programme after 1539 and to improve upon what had been accomplished then. In this flurry of defensive activity, England's limited and primitive military engineering establishment was stretched to the limits; hence (perhaps) increasing numbers of Italians were employed on their own or with Englishmen. One of the most interesting collaborations for our purposes took place at Tynemouth.

The Earl of Hertford had viewed the place in 1544 en route to invade Scotland and his possibly favourable impressions may have prompted the king in the late winter of 1544–45 to gather together a design team to assess the possibilities of the location. The three surveyors despatched north were Sir Richard Lee (knighted in 1544 for his part in Hertford's assault on Edinburgh) and two 'Italians expert in fortifying': Gian Tommaso Scala and Antonio da Bergamo.[44] Lee was clearly most struck by the site, judging it the most formidable in England as 'a place moste apte and nedeful to be fortyfied'. The three made a survey of the complicated possibilities offered by the monastery and the rolling terrain which stretched between it and the Tyne; by 16 February 1545 they were preparing plans how best to fortify it. Lee had emerged during the late 1530s working with John Rogers about Calais, but his work previous to this time was in the 'transitional' style of what Professor Hale calls the *retardataire* building of 1539–42.[45] Scala, on the other hand, already had considerable experience. It was almost certainly he who (in addition to his birds-eye-view of Newcastle, discussed earlier) prepared the one plan for the site made in 1545 which has survived (pl. 24).[46] The plan is not to any scale; indeed it is highly impressionistic and with few notations of distance. But Scala's conception for the defence of Tynemouth is quite explicit: two great angle-bastions, faced in ashlar, with flankers to guard the curtain wall while on the Tyne side was to be a platform with numerous casemated gun chambers and embrasures. This plan was revolutionary and it seems to be the earliest for the fortification of any English site to the new design technique.

Lee must have been impressed, for this very likely was the first occasion on which he could have learned how the *trace italienne* design operated, several months before Melloni's work at Fort d'Outreau became explicit. Scala in any case was convinced of the importance of his contribution to the discussion; in his memoirs he asserted 'fisi la forteza de timor [Tynemouth] che son sulla bocha de la fiumare de novo castel' and in his manuscript he penned a much more restrained, seemingly more accurate (if again, not to any scale) representation of his proposals for the site (pl. 25).[47] Nothing like what Scala proposed or remembered was apparently built. There was not enough time to undertake anything as complex as ashlar facing or casemated gun chambers and indeed what the massive workforce there accomplished in the five months between February and July was a big ditch and a very long earth wall. When the site was surveyed later in the century, no great Italianate bastions existed (pl. 26). But this is perhaps beside the point. The point is that this brief (Lee was back in London by 14 March) cooperation between two Italians and an Englishman may be one of the transmission points for the beginnings of Englishmen's knowledge of how the *trace italienne* worked.

A further piece of speculation concerns Lee's next important assignment – Portsmouth, seen to be under special threat from the French and visited by the king himself in July 1545. From the work of Professors Biddle and Harvey, it is fairly clear that during this summer, a remarkable map was prepared and new defences proposed, but as at Tynemouth, not executed as suggested (pl. 21). It is intriguing that modern aspects were pencilled, probably by someone working at Portsmouth, perhaps in 1546, onto the earlier 1545, 'transitional' proposals for the town's defence. In every case, such as the three angle-bastions with orillons and flankers, the pencilled additions were in this new idiom (pl. 27). So, it is, as Biddle asserts, 'by far the earliest scheme for defence of an English town by means of a fully-flanked bastion system in the Italian style'.[48] Lee's draughtsmanship cannot be proved, but if he was the penciller, cannot his interaction with Scala and Bergamo at Tynemouth earlier in the year be the origins of the suggested improvements at Portsmouth?

What is certain is that over the next two years Italianate forts were increasingly proposed and built and that numerous Italians were employed in Britain. The most sophisticated work was done in the Boulonnais, but there were some attempts, however feeble, to apply some Italian concepts to strengths built at Gravesend, Sandown, Southsea Castle, Sharpenode and then at Yarmouth Castle.[49] Scala continued after his time at Tynemouth to work in the north and in his memoires specified 'fisi la traversa a barvick et fisi quel de uarch [Wark]'. Bergamo went from Tynemouth straight to Holy Island where by 10 May 1545 a new fort was designed and staked out, 'with thadvice of the Italian engenere', who worked closely with two Englishmen, Thomas Gower and John Man.[50] Bergamo at some point also visited Wark and proposed a massive adaptation to the castle there on a signed plan

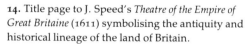

14. Title page to J. Speed's *Theatre of the Empire of Great Britaine* (1611) symbolising the antiquity and historical lineage of the land of Britain.

15. Title page to M. Drayton's *Poly-Olbion* (1612–22) also mirrors the antiquarian fervour of the period. The central figure of Albion, flanked by historical figures evoking 'Great Britaine's' past, is a young maiden holding a sceptre and a cornucopia and personifying *Britannia* wrapped in a 'cartographic cloak' to symbolise the land.

16. Map of the Isle of Lundy, Glamorgan, Monmouthshire and part of Brecknockshire from M. Drayton's *Poly-Olbion* (1612–22) is used to illustrate an allegorical poem about the traditionally disputed ownership of Lundy between England and Wales.

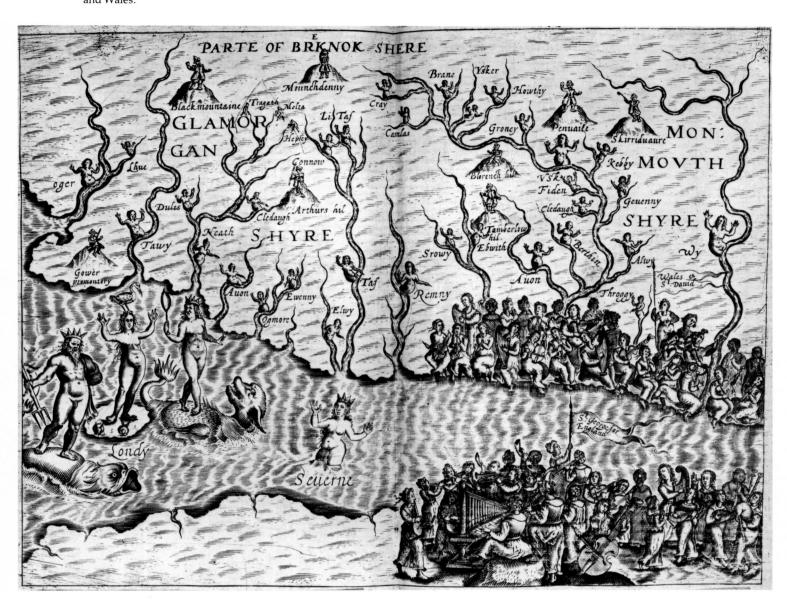

18. *(top)* The siege of Edinburgh Castle in 1573, showing the Castle Hill Bastion as it appeared then.

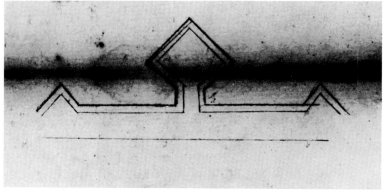

17. *(bottom)* The 'grocely pricked out' drawing of the Edinburgh Castle Hill Bulwark, 1548.

19. Gian Tommasso Scala's view of Newcastle 1545.

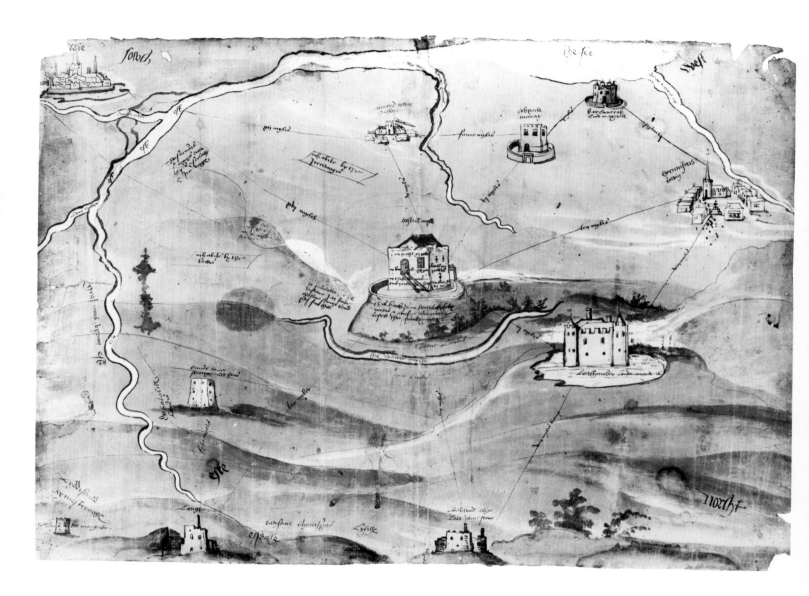

20. The map prepared in 1547 to show south-west
Scotland about Castlemilk.

21. Plan of the proposed defences for Portsmouth
1545.

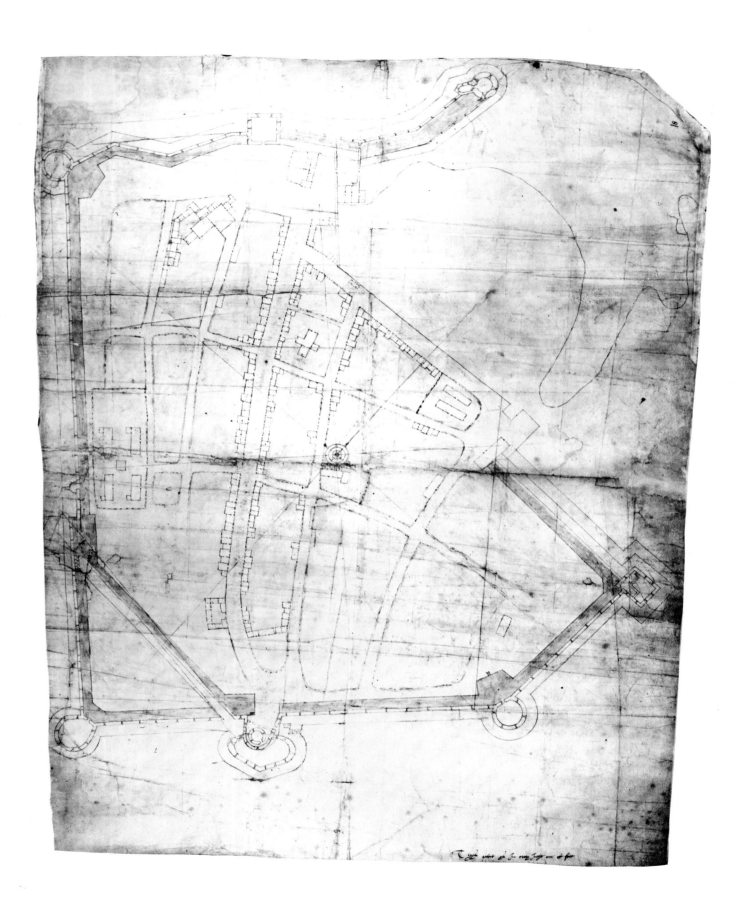

22. Fort d'Outreau as represented on the first survey of Boulogne 1545.

23. Fort d'Outreau as represented on the second survey of Boulogne 1546.

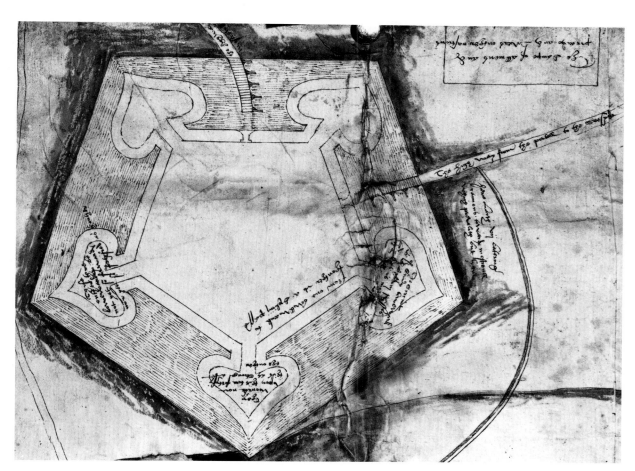

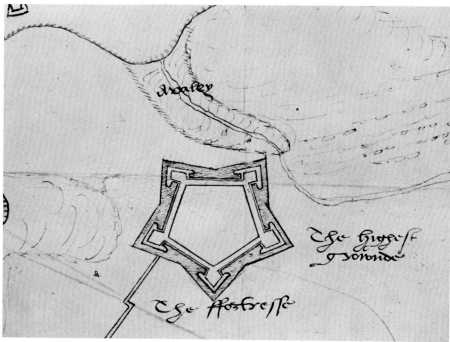

24. Scala's proposals for the fortification of
Tynemouth in 1545.

25. The defences of Tynemouth as Scala remembered them in his memoires.

26. Tynemouth as seen in 1580s.

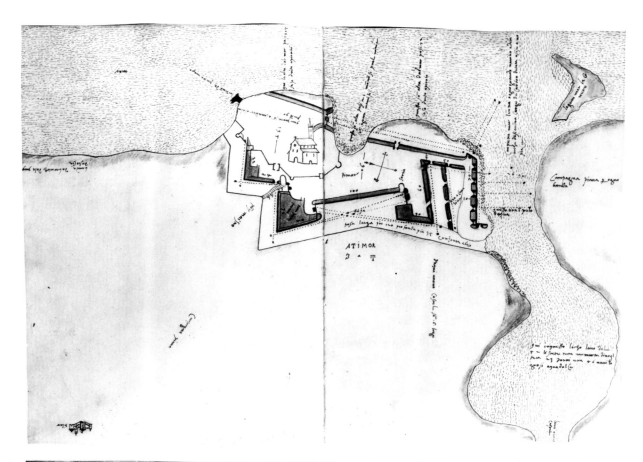

The pencilled proposals for the defence of
Portsmouth (inked-in for emphasis: cf. plate 21).

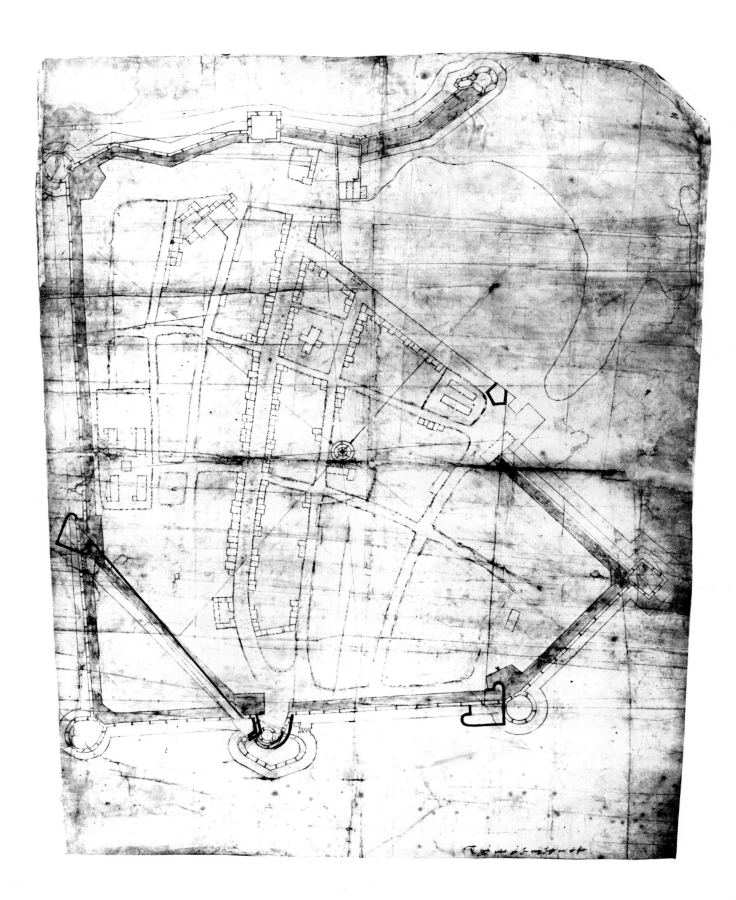

28. Rossetti's proposals for a fortress at Broughty in Scotland 1547.

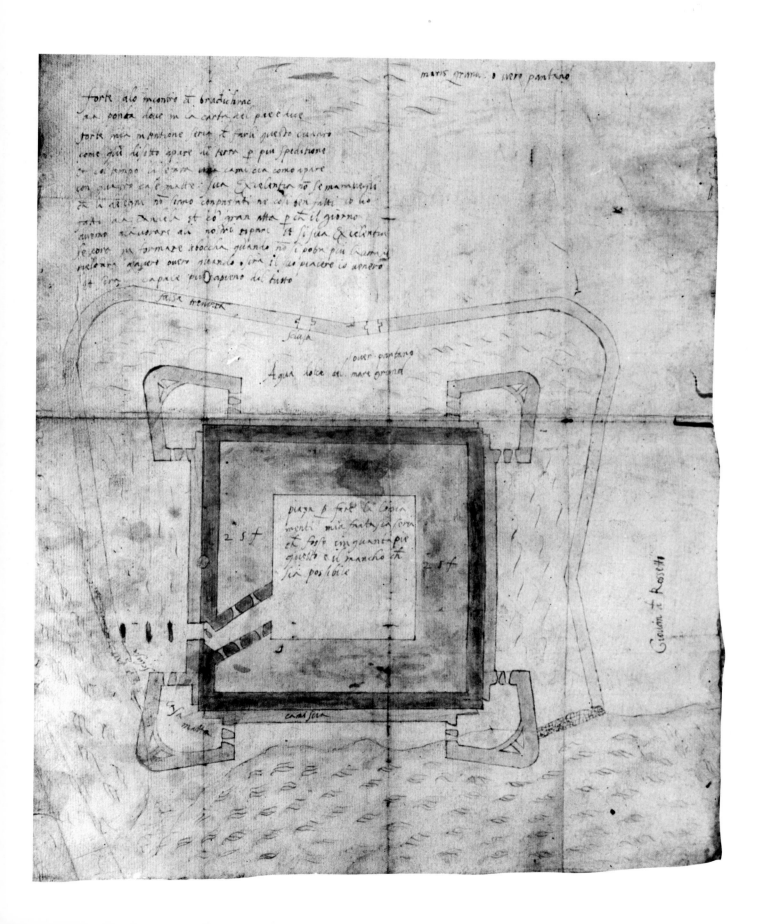

29. Eyemouth: designed by Sir Richard Lee in 1547; plat probably drawn in 1549, redrawn here.

30. Divider and Scale from the plat of Eyemouth.

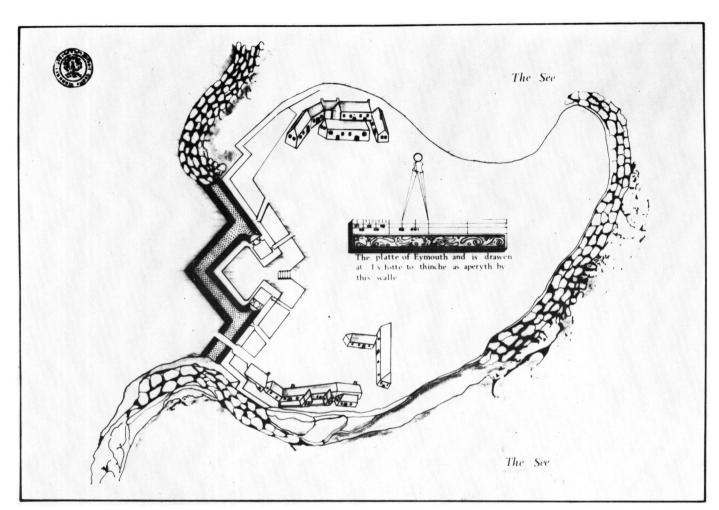

The See

The platte of Eymouth and is drawen at 1x fotte to thinche as aperyth by this scalle

The See

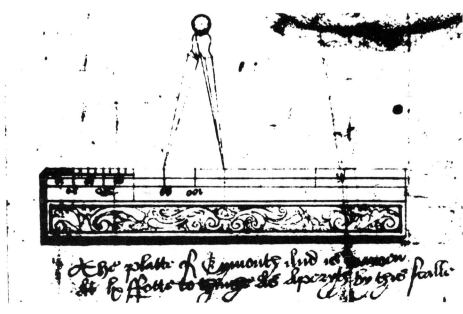

apparently to scale. Yet another Italian in the north was the famous Archangelo Arcano, noted both as an engineer, but also as 'the best gunner in England':[51] a craft increasingly influenced by mathematical ideas. Arcano too was at Wark, in February 1545, and then prepared in May a plat for Kelso which clearly proposed bastions able to provide flanking fire along the walls.[52] In 1547 he would be twice sent to St Andrews which was being held by Scottish rebels then being aided by Somerset.[53] Intriguingly, the French force led by Pietro and Leon Strozzi, two famous Italian captains with long careers in the service of Francis I and Henry II, which descended upon St Andrews in July 1547 and quickly recaptured it, also contained Antonio Melloni, architect of the great Fort d'Outreau which mirrored or perhaps inspired the English works at Boulogne.[54]

Another Italian active in the north was Giovanni di Rossetti, also known variously as 'Mr John the Ingineer' or 'the Italion' or 'the engenour' or to give him his title at Broughty 'Ingener Master of thordinaunce'.[55] First in Henry's service in 1543, he accompanied Arcano on his expeditions to St Andrews, then later in 1547 was appointed to modernise Broughty Castle which the English gained in September. While there he also made a number of proposals for new fortifications. The plan which survives for one of these, although not drawn to scale, does show a firm grasp of the *trace italienne* and how most efficiently to construct such forts (pl. 28).[56] He then found himself collaborating with Sir Thomas Palmer brought over from Boulogne (where he clearly had learned much about the new technology working with Rogers, Lee and Grey of Wilton) to design a bold and complex Italianate fortress overlooking Broughty Castle and the Tay. During 1548 and afterwards Rossetti was used extensively all over the north, advising twice over Holy Island, once at Berwick, then at Newcastle and inspecting the numerous new fortifications built by the English in Scotland.

English engineers were also rapidly applying the new technology, and increasingly were working alone, without Italian assistance. When Sir Richard Lee designed the new fortress at Eyemouth in September 1547, he made numerous mistakes, but he clearly grasped how to build a massive angle-bastion with flankers sunken behind orillons (pl. 29). Similarly Thomas Petyt executed a highly complicated and complex new *trace italienne* at Lauder in April. When Palmer and Grey of Wilton then set about constructing what was to be the largest and most sophisticated fortress at Hadding-ton, they clearly understood what they were about, for their mighty work there would do all that was asked of it: be built quickly, cost little and then withstand in July and August a furious siege by a powerful French army led by some of the most redoubtable captains in Europe. When Lee in September then turned to building yet another *trace italienne* fortress, at Dunglass, his increasingly mature appreciation of what it required was evident.[57] In late 1550, he and Palmer staked out a jewel of a *trace italienne* fortress with their proposed Berwick Citadel.[58] English comprehension and use of the new technology were now quite firm, both men having learned much in the 'school of war' which was Scotland during 1547–50.

Can any conclusions be drawn from this exposition of Anglo-Italian contacts and the acceptance by Englishmen of Italian design concepts? It is fairly probable that English appreciation of the *trace italienne* happened or was facilitated through these numerous contacts. Cannot the transmission of the value, mode of application and technology of scale map drawing also have occurred or at least have been reinforced in the same way? Perhaps, but we cannot ignore the fact that English scale maps were being executed before the work of Scala, Bergamo, Arcano and Rossetti.

It is true to say that these new fortifications depended in part for their success on the precision with which they were built: thickness of their walls was vital; the distance between the flankers (determined in part by the ordnance which was housed in them) and the dimensions of the flankers were also important (and would be a matter of intense debate during the 1540s and later); the degree of angle for the bastion was of note; so too the slope of the curtain walls. All of these factors called for some degree of mathematical precision and this may have encouraged the application of scales to plans. But this was also true of the 'transitional' forts of 1539–47. Another possible argument for the adaption at this time of scale drawings was that there were very few thoroughly skilled practitioners of the new craft. They were so overworked that often they could only survey a site and draw up a design before having to go elsewhere. The actual construction had to be left to surveyors not so knowledgeable who thus needed as detailed instructions as possible – yet another possible inducement to employ scales.

However, there is little denying that Englishmen were receptive to and intoxicated by Italian ideas: Palmer not only built Italianate forts, but he wrote in an italic hand; when John Man forwarded a plan to the king's commander in the north in August 1545, he termed it, as Hertford snorted, 'a dissegno, as he calleth it'. He must have picked up the term in his dealings with Bergamo; perhaps Englishmen similarly picked up how to draw to scale, as the charming execution of a divider and scale on the plat of Eyemouth (pl. 30) aptly attests.

1. Carlisle's report is to be found in J. Stevenson, *Selections . . . Illustrating the Reign of Mary, Queen of Scots, 1543–68* (Glasgow, 1837), p. 35, but reference should also be made to the original, BL Cotton MS, Caligula, B. VII, f 339 (new foliation).
2. The best accounts are in M.L. Bush, *The Government Policy of Protector Somerset* (London, 1975), pp. 7–39 and G. Donaldson, *Scotland: James V – James VII* (Edinburgh, 1965), pp. 63–80.
3. The design for Haddington is discussed in *The History of the King's Works*, edited by H.M. Colvin. (London, 1982), IV, pp. 717–21.
4. F.W. Steer, 'A Map Illustrating the Siege of Leith, 1560' *Proceedings of the Society of Antiquaries of Scotland* (1961–2), 280–83 and plate L.
5. I. MacIvor, 'Artillery and Major Places of Strength in the Lothians and the East Border, 1513–1542' in D. Caldwell, *Scottish Weapons and Fortifications 1100–1800* (Edinburgh, 1981), pp. 146–48.
6. *Calendar of State Papers, Spanish*, ix (1547–9), p. 246. I have not been able to consult the original of this grant.
7. Ubaldini's two letters are preserved in the National Library of Scotland, Advocates MS 29. 2. 3, nos. 143–4. I am grateful to Dr Richard Cooper for transcription and translation of these. Dunbar is described by I. MacIvor (1981), pp. 94–132.
8. *Accounts of the Lord High Treasurer of Scotland*, ix (1546–50), p. 163 and so also pp. 281 and 444–46, 464.
9. *Accounts*, pp. 361, 405.
10. Such is asserted in the entry for him in *DNB*.
11. Ubaldini's original manuscript is BL Royal MS 13A VIII. The Bannatyne Club reprinted it in 1829; for the original, consult the libraries indicated in *Short Title Catalogue of Books Published in England, 1450–1660*, edited by A. Pollard and G. Redgrave (London, 1950), no. 24480.
12. BL Additional MS 10, 169, ff. 1–125; see f. 110v.
13. R.A. Skelton, 'The Military Surveyor's Contribution to British Cartography in the 16th Century', *Imago Mundi*, 24 (1970), 77–85; see also R.A. Skelton and J. Summerson, *A Description of Maps and Architectural Drawings . . . at Hatfield House* (London, 1971), pp. 28–30.
14. L.R. Shelby, *John Rogers – Tudor Military Engineer* (Oxford, 1967), pp. 5–48 (esp. 30–41); 127–63.
15. C.H. Carter, *The Western European Powers, 1500–1700* (London, 1971), p. 287.
16. G.R. Elton, *Policy and Police* (Cambridge, 1972), p. 207.
17. P.D.A. Harvey, 'The Portsmouth Map of 1545 and the Introduction of Scale Maps into England', *Hampshire Studies* (Portsmouth, 1981), 33–49.
18. Harvey, 'Portsmouth Map', 35–36 and see R.A. Skelton and P.D.A. Harvey, *Local Maps and Plans from Medieval England* (Oxford, 1981), introduction and chapter 4.
19. Hatfield House, CPM I. 65.
20. M. Merriman, 'The Platte of Castlemilk, 1547', *Transactions of the Dumfriesshire and Galloway Natural History and Antiquarian Society* 44 (1967), 175–81.
21. Harvey, 'Portsmouth Map,' p. 35.
22. Harvey, 'Portsmouth Map,' p. 45.
23. P.D.A. Harvey, *The History of Topographical Maps* (London, 1980) is the best introduction to this topic; see especially pp. 55–103, 153–68.
24. For M. Biddle on Portsmouth, see *The King's Works*, IV, pp. 490–510.
25. Shelby, plates 20–21.
26. These plans are discussed in *The King's Works*, IV, pp. 698–725.
27. Harvey, 'Portsmouth Map', p. 40.
28. Discussed by both Harvey in 'Portsmouth Map', p. 41 and J. Hale in *The King's Works*, IV, pp. 378–79, 385.
29. Rossetti and Arcano are discussed below, pp. 63–65.
30. See Harvey, 'Portsmouth Map', pp.40–4 and Hale, *The King's Works*, IV, pp. 388, 392–93.
31. See *The King's Works*, IV, fig. 64 and pp. 702–703.
32. Shelby, plates 15–22.
33. Steer, p. 280.
34. Bush, p. 28.
35. *The King's Works*, IV, pp. 384–86.
36. *Correspondance politique de Odet de Selve*, ed. G. Lefevre-Pontalis (Paris, 1888), p. 360.
37. N. Tartaglia, *Quesiti e Inventioni diverse* (Venice, 1546), lib. 6, *quesito* 6. Note Professor Hale's remark that a copy was sent to England in 1546, the year of its second edition, in *The King's Works*, IV, p. 385, n.3.
38. See Hale in *The King's Works*, IV, pp. 386–87.
39. Shelby, pp. 62, 66–67, 71.
40. Shelby, plate 19.
41. Shelby, pp. 100, 103, 107, 143; plates 20–2.
42. *The King's Works*, III, pp. 383–93, plates 40–44; Shelby, pp. 59–85, plates 14–22.
43. R.B. Wernham, *Before the Armada: The Growth of English Foreign Policy 1485–1588* (London, 1966), pp. 158–61.
44. See *The King's Works*, IV, pp. 682–84.
45. *The King's Works*, IV, p. 377.
46. BL Cotton MS Augustus I. ii. 7 (published in *Archaeologia Aeliana*, 1898, facing p. 68).
47. His memoirs (discussed by L. White, 'Jacopo Aconcio as an engineer', *American Historical Review*, 1967, p. 431, n. 18) are in Turin, Biblioteca Reale, MS militare 377; the quotation occurs on f. 47v; the plan on ff. 13v–14r; it may have been used by G.B. Belici for his plan of Tynemouth: *Nuova inventione di fabricar fortezze* (Venice, 1598).
48. *The King's works*, IV, pp. 504–506.
49. V.T.C. Smith, 'The Milton Blockhouse, Gravesend: Research and Excavation', *Archaeologia Cantiana* 76 (1980), 341–62; J.R. Kenyon, 'An Aspect of the 1559 Survey of the Isle of Wright', *Post-Medieval Archaeology* 13 (1979), 61–77; but see also *The King's Works*, IV, pp. 393–4, 550–63, 565–69, 602–603.
50. *The King's Works*, IV, pp. 675–76.
51. So the Scottish ambassador reported from London. See *Scottish Correspondence of Mary of Lorraine*, edited by A.I. Cameron, (Edinburgh, 1927), p. 184.
52. '4 balwarkes to flank yt abowt'. *Hamilton Papers* II, p. 544.
53. *Calendar of State Papers Relating to Scotland and Mary Queen of Scots, 1547–1603*, I, no. 14; *Acts of the Privy council of England*, II, p. 90; 1547–49, p. 90; *Spanish*, IX, p. 102.
54. C. Primo, *Della vita e delle opere degl'italiani scrittori di artiglieria e meccanica militare . . . 1286–1560* (Turin, 1841), p. 87.
55. See *The King's Works*, IV, pp. 700–701.
56. Hatfield House, Salisbury MS, vol. 205, no. 78. I am grateful to the Marquis of Salisbury for permission to publish this plan.
57. For this Scottish experience, see *The King's Works*, IV, pp. 702–26.
58. *The King's Works*, IV, pp. 642–46.

Peter Eden

Three Elizabethan estate surveyors: Peter Kempe, Thomas Clerke and Thomas Langdon

There can be few historians of the Elizabethan age who have not had occasion to mention the first William Cecil, Lord Burghley. He was at or near the centre of the political stage for most of his long life, and his capacity for detail was such that scarcely any aspect of Elizabethan economy and society was outside his interest.

To bring Cecil in thus at the outset might look like mere lip service to an academic convention. But, as will emerge, the three Elizabethan estate surveyors who are the subject of this biographical essay are successive heirs to a tradition originating in Cecil's household and extending over a century from the accession of Elizabeth I. The fortunate survival of the wills of all three men (those of Peter Kempe, d 1576/7; of Thomas Clerke, d 1592; and of Thomas Langdon, d 1638) supplemented by fairly copious documentation (not least the maps made by Clerke and Langdon for five Oxford colleges, with corresponding account rolls) permits the reconstruction of this tradition in unmistakable outline, if with some gaps and uncertainties in detail.[1]

Cecil's interest in the arts and emerging technologies has often been remarked. Beckingsale's biography, for instance, devotes an entire chapter to this theme: John Dee, describing 'how mathematics could be applied by merchants, lawyers, soldiers, goldsmiths, doctors, navigators, geographers, surveyors, architects and others in their practical work' was but 'preaching what Burghley encouraged in practice'[2]. But did this encouragement extend to estate management; and in particular what evidence is there that Cecil, who was an important landowner, contributed as patron to innovations in land measurement and mapping?

The period 1558–1598 was one of great change in surveying practice. At its commencement estate maps were a rarity; by the end of it they were a commonplace. At the time of Elizabeth's accession land holdings were still normally described in written form, using square measure based on an acre which might be, but often was not, a statute acre. Such written descriptions were commonly copies of manorial records, though they certainly were sometimes based on recent field measurement. Alternatively parcels might be specified by relating them to their abuttals, with or without orientation. Infrequently rectilinear diagrams were provided to enable the descriptions to be followed more easily. It is tempting to think of such diagrams as primitive maps, although they hardly constitute a distinct stage in the evolutionary process. Panoramas – obliques as seen by a surveyor-bird – were another form of illustration, but these of their nature could not be to scale. By the time of Cecil's death techniques of measuring and drawing were fully developed, though cartographic embellishment long continued to recall the earlier panoramas, with buildings and other features shown in consistent or fragmented perspective. Was informed patronage a significant factor in this rapid development?

Cecil is usually thought of as a cautious man. With him to be informed was to be forearmed. He was a glutton for parchment and paper. His records served not only for reference but also as strong-points for defensive or offensive action in the conduct of affairs. The planning of the inner court at Theobalds in the early 1570s included provision for 'an evidence howse' located in a 'single chamber at the west end of the gallery'. The chosen position, a usual one, was presumably preferred because it was relatively fire- and burglar-proof[3].

Offices held by Cecil during the comparatively early stages of his career were of the kind that can hardly have failed to bring him to reflect on the problems of documenting landed estates. In 1549–50 he became Surveyor to the Princess Elizabeth. He was not yet thirty; the future Queen was still in her teens. The post was apparently filled by a deputy, a common practice at the time, and Cecil's supervision may not have been very close. In any case such a surveyorship in the mid sixteenth century was not primarily or even at all concerned with mapping. A contemporary document describes the duties involved at some length without any allusion to quantification apart from a few vague references to 'acres'. Such definitions remained current in legal encyclopaedias at least until the last decade of the reign.[4] But however indirectly Cecil was involved it is likely that he would have taken more than a nominal interest in his young mistress's property. He cannot have failed to appreciate that the absence of precise information about the whereabouts, boundaries and content of scattered estates could be a disadvantage in an increasingly litigious age.

In 1561 Cecil became Master of the Court of Wards, a position which he held for the rest of his life. It was the task of its officials to inform themselves about the location and extent of lands subject to wardship with a view to extracting as much as possible from guardians and preventing fraud. Thomas Seckford of Woodbridge, Christopher Saxton's patron, was surveyor to the Court. Cecil as Master must have approved the patronage if he did not actually inspire it. He is known to have taken an active interest in the course of the undertaking. The surveys made between 1573 (or earlier) and 1579 for Saxton's Atlas no doubt made use of everything that was accessible in the way of existing information and the resources of the Court cannot have been overlooked. It is still possible, perhaps, that its extensive records may shed some light on this question[5].

Some interest on Cecil's part in the potentialities of local mapping and in the techniques involved is presumably to be inferred from this background. In the fields of public and foreign policy Cecil's positive conviction of the importance of cartography are more evident. His own map collections include items annotated by him and there have even survived a number of sketches in his hand, such as that of Liddesdale on the Scottish border, believed to date from c1561[6]. But such productions are no evidence of specialised know-how and are quite likely to be copies. Cecil emerges as a consumer rather than a producer of maps, concerned primarily with the larger realities of statecraft.

By comparison with these official concerns Cecil's annotations of estate papers have attracted little attention, although they speak unmistakably for his concern with the management of his own property. An unascribed map, now at Hatfield House, of lands between Enfield and Tottenham was glossed by him at an unknown date (pl.

31)[7]. Such private matters are likely to have occupied less of his time at the height of his career, though he no doubt gave periodic attention to them. So late as 1593 we find him adding notes about land use and tenure to a map of Cliffe Park, Northants, prepared for him by his steward, Richard Shute[8] (pl. 32).

These look like the operations of a systematic man who managed to find at least some time to see to his private interests. There is little to suggest any underlying spirit of patronage so far as the emergent profession of land surveying is concerned. In his dealings with Ralph Agas, with whom he corresponded and who may indeed have been his tenant[9] the little there is to go on suggests that Cecil, though approachable, was not munificent. As late as the 1590s Agas was writing to him about drainage problems in the Lincolnshire Fens and deploring the dearth of estate maps in the area. The surveyor's tone is respectful but not without a note of criticism. Nowhere is it implied that the great landowner had been a pioneer.[10]

It is thus not surprising that Cecil's own household, as described by Barnett[11], does not seem to have included a land surveyor as such. Peter Kempe, with whom this story really begins, was ostensibly a land steward of the old type, more concerned with the manor court than with topographical realities, although proof to the contrary may yet come to light. He was in Cecil's employ from 1560 at latest till his death in December or January 1576/7. Thereafter Richard Shute (who was previously connected with the Court of Wards) occupied a similar position. Shute outlived his master but disappears from view about the turn of the century, having fallen latterly into disfavour[12]. Peter Kempe's will, drawn up very shortly before his death, is brief, but its terms make the close relationship to Thomas Clerke clear, for the latter receives a legacy of £20 as well as being one of three witnesses. That the Thomas Clerke of Kempe's will is in fact the surveyor of that name is proved by the terms of Clerke's own will, requesting that he should be buried alongside his old master. Thomas Clerke's relationship with Peter Kempe at the time when the will was made one of at least four years duration, even supposing that Clerke left Cecil's service before 1577. A list of servants at Theobalds made by Cecil 'ageinst the Q[ueen's] Ma[jesty] comyng thyther' in 1572 includes the names of both men. Kempe is to be 'clerk of ye kytchin for ye lordship first table', Clerke a waiter.[13] This is the first known mention of Clerke, but he was not necessarily a newcomer. We may assume that Clerke as Kempe's assistant was given a grounding in estate management but there is no indication of how he learned to measure land.

After 1577 Clerke may have continued to work at Burghley with Shute as steward though he had perhaps hoped for Kempe's job. At any rate Clerke and Shute remained on good terms to judge by the bequest made to Shute by Clerke. Clerke's earliest known map[14], of the Panworth Hall estate in Ashill Norfolk (pl. 33), was made for one Thomas Huggon (otherwise Hagon) in 1581; it is now at Holkham Hall, the estate having been acquired by Chief Justice Coke in 1590 (pl. 33). The title does not describe the surveyor as 'of Stamford St Martin', a style he used subsequently. At the time of his death in 1592 Clerke had been resident in the parish for six years at least. The baptism of Thomas, the first of his five children, took place on 29 April 1586 (he was buried the next day); the remainder followed at appropriate intervals ending with Elizabeth on October 8 1590[15].

So far as is known it was in 1586 that Clerke's association with All Souls College Oxford began. His survey of Whatborough in Leicestershire and the background to it have been described by M.W. Beresford[16]. Clerke was appointed surveyor to an Exchequer Commission set up in that year to determine a dispute between the College and Henry Lord Cromwell as to lordship. Henry's better known grandfather had acquired adjoining lands at the dissolution of Launde Priory. Whatborough had been held by the Priory on long leases at least since 1458. Several maps of Whatborough based on Clerke's survey are held at All Souls. Perhaps the most interesting of these is the mock-up for a large piece, presumably intended for the Court, an unusual scissors-and-paste affair which reveals how one Elizabethan surveyor set about the problems of design and embellishment.[17]

The Whatborough survey of 1586 was not, strictly speaking, carried out for the College. As a party to the dispute the latter would have been responsible for a share of the costs and may have been in a position to influence the choice of surveyor. Shortly after the Whatborough job, Clerke measured some of the All Souls properties in Kent. A number of corresponding maps[18] carry his name and are perhaps by him, though one (unclassified) is 'made according to the platte of Mr Tho. Clerke drawn in March Anno Eliza. . . . xxxj° by Tho. Langdon'. The Computus Rolls, which from 1591 to 1605 provide detailed records of the college outlay on mapping its estates elsewhere, make no mention of these Kentish surveys.[19] Possibly the Warden, a prime mover in these estate matters and himself a man of Kent, provided the wherewithal from a different source.

Some support for this conjecture may be had from the circumstances of a dispute with no less a person than the Queen in which the Warden and Fellows had recently been involved. In or about 1569 the College had leased some woodland in Middlesex to Hovenden's brother Christopher on terms which were subsequently admitted to have been disadvantageous to the foundation. Two years later the lease was surrendered. The indiscretion did not pass unnoticed in high places and in 1587 a letter was sent to the College on behalf of the Queen calling on the College to make a lease of the woodland on similar terms to a Lady Jane Stafford. Cecil, who initially pressed the College to comply, appears to have written later in the same year to Hovenden charging him with nepotism and with negligence in granting the lease to his brother without first having a proper survey made. The Warden replied in September pleading that the generous terms of the lease had been an oversight; and that 'for surveighing, neither tyme betwene my resolution to make a lease and the demising woulde permitt the same: nor yet were the companie ever willing to be at so great a charge'. The context probably implies measuring and mapping since the delay and expense put forward as excuse would not apply so convincingly to the perfunctory processes of a manorial court. Hovenden was in a fix. Lady Stafford's partisans made mincemeat of the College's arguments. Hovenden may well have paid for the Kentish maps, but in the long run this experience was probably enough to induce the Fellows to embark on the comprehensive surveying program which began soon afterwards. As the College's opponents had pointed out, there was plenty of money in the kitty.[20]

About the time of these Kentish surveys Clerke was again in East Anglia, this time in the employ of the formidable Lady Ann, widow of Sir Thomas Gresham who on his death in 1579 left to her outright a substantial part of his extensive estates[21]. On 28 February 1587, Thomas Read, Lady Gresham's grandson by her first husband, married Mildred, third daughter of Sir Thomas Cecil[22]. The two families had long been intimate. The surveys were presumably made in connection with the corresponding settlement. A letter written by Clerke from Stamford in September of the same year to Read, then at Massingham in Norfolk, explains that he is prevented from completing his survey there by unsuitable weather, the late harvest and personal engagements[23]. A map by Clerke of Earl Stonham Suffolk, originally of 1587 but known only from a 19th-century copy, was presumably part of the same operation, the manor being another Gresham property[24].

In addition to these surveys Clerke was also steward to Lady Gresham for her manor of Borrowhall in Holkham Norfolk. Here he became involved in a wrangle over foldcourse with a Duchy of Lancaster tenant which rumbled on in the courts for at least a decade. Clerke's map of Borrowhall, made for his patroness in 1590 no doubt in connection with this dispute, is now at Holkham Hall[25] (pl. 34).

In 1591 Clerke was once more working for All Souls, this time at Padbury in Buckinghamshire. His map 'begun[n]e the first daye of September A° dni 1591' was 'ended by Thomas Langdon late servaunte to the said Tho. Clerke'. Payments in the Computus Roll for that year under the head 'summa equitantium' include £5 to him for surveying at Padbury and two disbursements for his lodging there. A note added at the end of 'variae expensae' includes 'xiid to Mr Clark's man at Padburie'. There is no doubt that this refers to Langdon as in 1592 the roll includes the item 'xxs to Mr Clark his man towards the plotting of Padburie in parte of payment'[26]. The wording of the title to the Padbury map suggests that Langdon must have completed it shortly after Clerke's death.

The Padbury survey must have been Clerke's last job for All Souls. It may be surmised that he returned to Stamford towards the end of 1591. He died there in the following year and was buried on 20 June, it is to be hoped alongside his old master, Peter Kempe, as he had desired[27].

Nothing can be said for certain about Thomas Clerke's early life. He must have come from a gentry family and may well have completed his education at Oxford or Cambridge, perhaps followed by a spell at one of the Inns of Court. No doubt he knew what he was about when he 'claymed the common lynge to be ye lady Greshams her freehoulde & caused her sheepe to be putt thereon and likewise caused a pownde to be erected uppon the Moore clayminge ye same to be her freehoulde'. He could be the Thomas Clerke of Avington who was admitted to the Inner Temple in November 1567, but this identification raises problems. If he was a contemporary of Barnaby Googe (another of the servitors on Cecil's 1572 list) he could have been like him born c1540. If his 'brother-in-law' Thomas Dandie is to be equated with the Thomas Dandie Esquire of Combs in Suffolk (d 1607) recorded by Anthony Norris, East Anglian origins are perhaps to be inferred[28]. All this is surmise.

Langdon in 1589 must have been young, perhaps still an undergraduate at New College. He had probably been helping Clerke for a year or two, and may be the assistant mentioned in Clerke's letter to Read already cited. However, neither the College nor the University have any record of him until ten years later when he petitioned for the degree of B.C.L. on 25 June and was admitted on 2 July. The petition recites that he was an M.A. of New College and had been studying civil law for three years[29]. Thomas Langdon had, as we learn from his will, a kinsman of the same name, and this raises the possibility that the graduand of 1599 is not the same man as Clerke's assistant. Here fortunately the language of the All Souls Computus

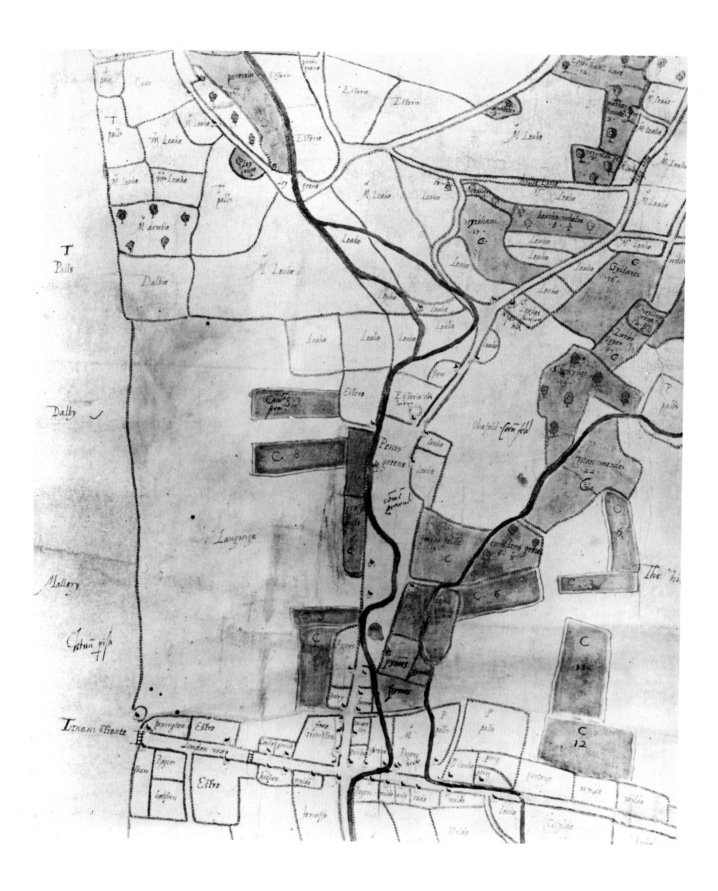

31. A map of the lands lying between Enfield and Tottenham. Annotated by Lord Burghley.

32. A map of Cliffe Park, Northamptonshire, drawn
by Richard Shute for Lord Burghley.

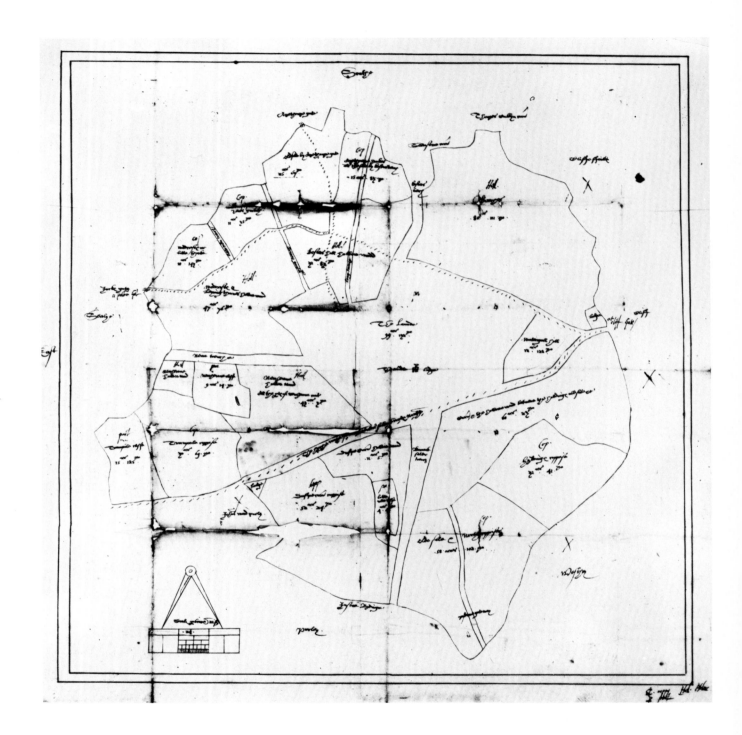

33. Thomas Clerke's map of the Panworth Hall estate in Ashill, Norfolk, 1581: detail showing title cartouche.

34. Thomas Clerke's map of Borrowhall in Holkham, Norfolk 1590: detail showing title cartoûche.

35a and **b.** Comparative cartographic details from Thomas Langdon's maps of Gamlingay Cambs. (1601) and copies by William Cole of Bletchley (1767). Merton Records 6.17 Map 1 and 6.19 Map 1.
35b. The second hand is presumably that of Cole's assistant, Edward Welles.

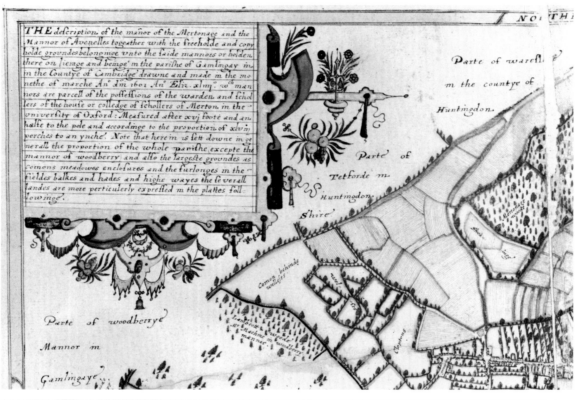

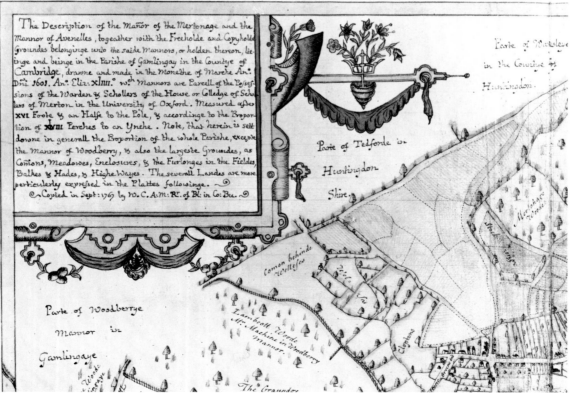

36a. Comparative cartographic details from Langdon's maps of Gamlingay, Cambs. and copies by William Cole of Bletchley (1767). Merton Records 6.17, map 2 and 6.19 map 2.
36b. Cole has copied the cartouche quite closely but added a characteristic embellishment.

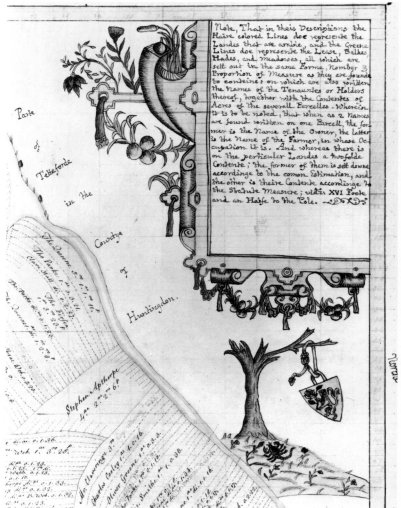

37a. Comparative cartographic details from Langdon's maps of Gamlingay, Cambs. and copies by William Cole of Bletchley (1767). Merton Records 6.17 map 4, and 6.19 map 4.
37b. Cole's version of the scale bar includes two shields of arms.

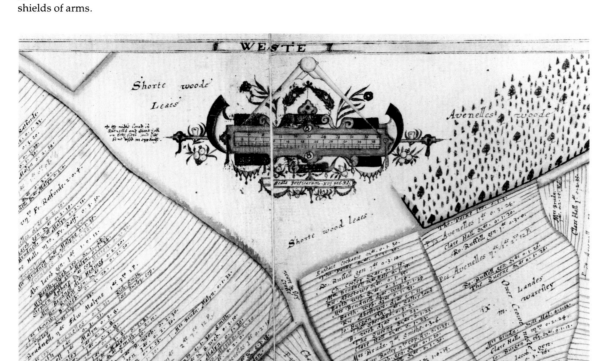

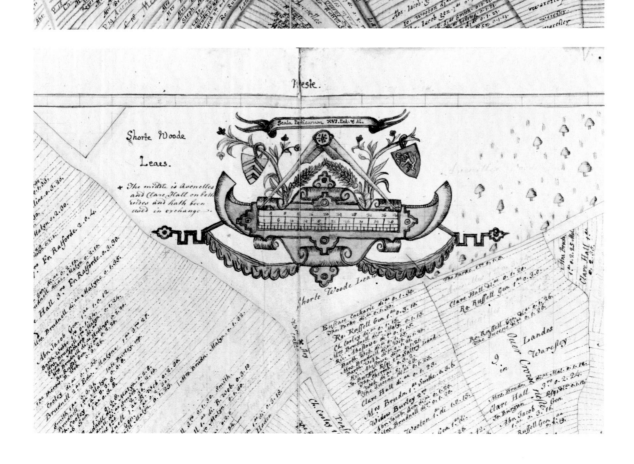

38a and **b.** Comparative cartographic details from
Langdon's maps of Gamlingay, Cambs. and copies
by William Cole of Bletchley (1767). Merton Records
6.17 map 14 and 6.19 map 14.

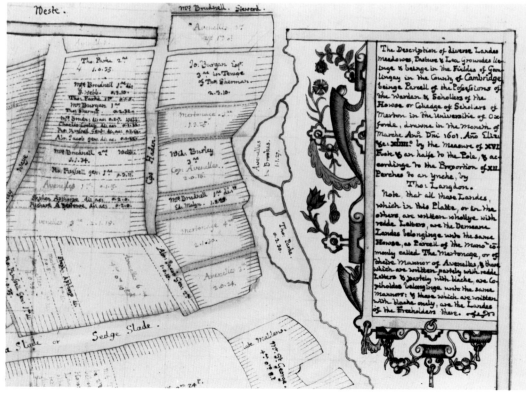

39a and **b.** Comparative cartographic details from Langdon's maps of Gamlingay, Cambs. and copies by William Cole of Bletchley (1767). Merton Records 6.17 map 14 and 6.19 map 14.

The two versions show 'Mr. St. George his howse' in identical form. The place is perhaps to be identified with the modern Hatley Park Farm.

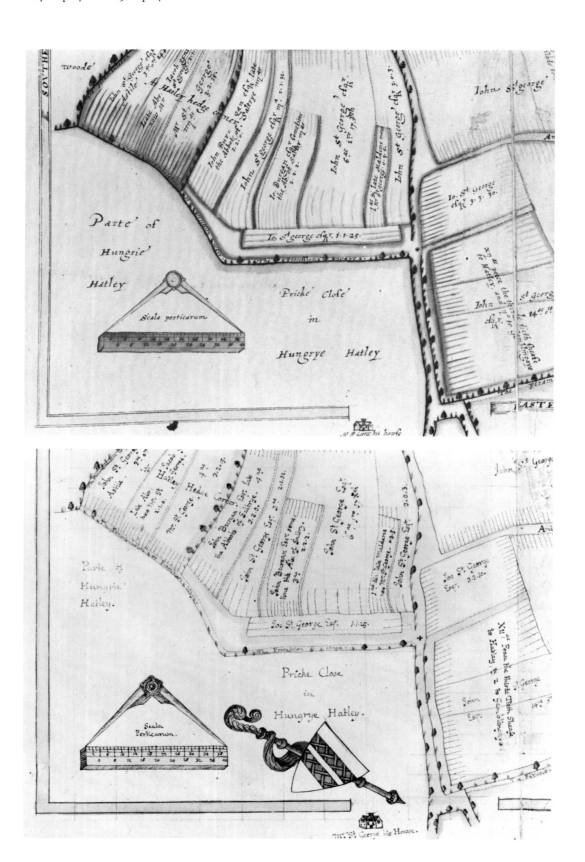

Rolls comes to our aid. These, which refer to him initially as 'Mr Clark's man', then in 1593 as 'the plotter' and in 1594 as 'Tho Langdon the Plotter' describe him in 1599 for the first time and thereafter as 'Mr Thomas Langdon', no doubt in deference to his new status.

After Clerke's rather abrupt departure from Oxford, Langdon was left with various matters at All Souls to tidy up in addition to the Padbury map. As the entry from the 1592 roll quoted above is the only reference to Langdon in it, one may surmise that he was in other parts of the country during the latter part of the year and into 1593. He evidently felt obliged to assume his late master's obligations to Lady Gresham. In September her agent at Massingham (where there was more trouble about sheep, this time with the Bedingfields of Oxborough) wrote to her that Langdon and a certain Mr Vicars were expected and would sort things out when they came[30]. In May 1593 he made a written survey and valuation of the manor of Emhouses in East Walton, Norfolk, for her behalf, adding at the end 'there are diverse Rents both free and copie in Gayton that are denyed to be paide, ffor that for want of a Terrar to Bounde out the landes for which the same is due, distresses can not rightly be taken'[31]. He was however back with the College in that year. It was to be one of intense activity, with field work going on in Kent, Sussex, Leicestershire and Shropshire. He received payments of £16 6s 8d during the year clear of expenses and made some 24 maps including at least 12 in September alone.

For the next year Langdon continued in the College's employ. Over a period of some 15 years from 1590 I calculate that he received a total of £161 11s 4d, the peak year being 1597 when his takings grossed £32 16s 3d. From time to time a daily rate is mentioned, usually 2s 6d, but on one occasion 4s. These payments represent his fees. In 1594 there were the following incidentals:

ijs vjd for the plotters horsmeat ij days iij nights

vid for a day and a nights grasse for ye plotters horse

xxd for washing Mr Carter & the Plotter

iis iijd for washing Mr Carter & Thomas Landon

vijs vid spent at Whatley by Thomas Langdon when he plotted the ground there ut patet per billam,

and in 1598:

xs viijd for Mr Beaumont & Mr Langdons charges at Leuckner ut patet per billam.

There were also disbursements for assistants. In 1660 the entry for

xs to a labourer for x dayes work at Egware with Mr Langdon

furnishes a useful standard of comparison for skilled and unskilled day rates. In 1604:

xxs to Robert Freeman for his paynes in carying the chayne with Mr Langdon in the Welsh progresse[32]

The position as regards instruments and materials was rather different. Instruments are not mentioned and surveyors often (though not invariably) provided their own. We know that Langdon had inherited some from his predecessor. They were expensive things. Initially, between 1593 and 1595 all materials appear to have been supplied by the College. Corresponding entries include:

ixs for xii skins of parchment for ye plotter
vd to the apoticarie for virmilion and lamp blake for ye plotter
ijd to ye painter for grindinge these colors

xijd for coloring for Thomas Landon

ijd for verditure to the Plotter
ijd for lin[. . .]seed oyle and a glasse for the plotter.

Later the College continued to supply parchment (a normal arrangement) but other items do not occur. So presumably the surveyor had to find them.

In 1605 there is a noticeable change in the tone of the All Souls accounts. It is apparent that the College is cutting down on expenditure and making use of the fellows to carry out at least some of the survey work:

iiij li xviijs vjd for Mr Bysse and Langdons Expenses in plottinge Southpetherton ut patet per billam
lijs for Mr Subwardens and Mr Langdons Expenses in plottinge Staunton Harcott ut patet per billam
xlvs ixd for Mr Subwardens Expenses in plottinge the land at Bozeat &c ut patet per billam.

Evidently the financial situation was deteriorating. In 1606 payments to Langdon ceased, and in the following year the College was borrowing money and selling timber.

Soon after proceeding to his second degree, Langdon's own New College commissioned him to measure and map their woodlands in the two Buckinghamshire parishes of Oakley and Tingewick. The atlas which contains them also includes four maps by John Hulett dated 1654. In addition the drafts for Langdon's maps survive in the muniments[33]. The Bursar's Rolls for 1600–01 include the entry:

So[lutum] magistro Langdon pro dimensione Boscorum   v li.
So[lutum] eidem pro libro in quo ea dimensio pulchre describitur   iiijs vjd.

Langdon does not appear to have done any other work for New College.

A year or so later he was measuring Merton College's property at Gamlingay in Cambridgeshire. The corresponding maps, in atlas form, are still preserved in the College (pl. 35–39). Nathaniel Brent, then Bursar, accompanied Langdon and supervised his work. The rolls record that Brent was paid £15 11s 10d, plus 25s for accommodation and 4s to a servant who went with them. From the College Register it appears that these were global figures and that Langdon actually received £12:

Codex   Item permissum est officiariis ut pasciscerentur cum magistro Langdon pro
topographicus   tabulis topographicis quas de terris nostris Gamlingeiensibus pulcherrime
                     descripserat quo paulo post peracto tradiderunt ei isto nomine duodecim
                     libras[34].

Also held by the College are a set of 18th-century copies of Langdon's maps of Gamlingay (pl. 35–39). These were made in 1767 by the antiquary William Cole for his crony Robert Masters, rector of Landbeach. Cole was assisted by Edward Welles, a retired schoolmaster then living at Water Eaton near Bletchley[35].

Towards the end of the year 1605, the last in which payments to him by All Souls are recorded, Langdon began working for Corpus Christi College. Here he followed on the heels of a certain Matthew Nelson who had been surveying for the College between 1602 and 1604 in Bedfordshire, Kent and Gloucestershire (pl. 40). Six maps survive in the muniments, only one of which is signed, but there are a number of payments recorded in the Liber Magnus[36]. Twenty years earlier the Oxfordshire, Berkshire, Gloucestershire and Bedfordshire estates had been 'surveyed' by Ralph Agas, but Agas's neatly written terriers do not suggest measurement and the payments to him (under the head 'impensae equitantium'), unless incomplete, do not seem high enough to cover extensive field work. Nelson is not otherwise known. His cartographic style, featuring compass roses with crosslet East points and rhumb lines (in one case intersecting) may reflect a chart-making tradition.

Langdon made some 16 maps for Corpus in the course of 1606, starting with estates in the vicinity of Oxford. A number of these maps are unsigned, but their style closely resembles that of others which carry Langdon's name or initials. Payments to him under the heads 'impensae placitorum' and 'impensae e cista finium' total £12 2s [?8]d in 1605, £16 in 1606 and £34 11s 2d in 1607. Extras include in 1606 'To Vallence his brother for seaven daies helping in the survey iiis vjd'. This was not lavish remuneration, perhaps just pocket money.

In 1607 Langdon worked for a short time for Brasenose College at Burrough on the Hill in Leicestershire. His three maps are in the College library. The Senior Bursar's Rolls (all that survive for this time) are evidently summaries and no payments for maps are recorded.

During 1608 Corpus seems to have diverted its surplus resources to buildings. The financing of a program of estate surveying must often have involved postponing expenditure in other directions and in reverse been suspended in order to build, or even (in the case of an academic institution) replenish the library. There was no real equivalent of a bank loan at this period and it was usual for landowners to plan their outlay a year at a time according to the income available from their rents. These last could, as already noticed, be boosted by selling capital assets such as standing timber. There was at least a relative lack of flexibility. However in 1609 Langdon was again working for Corpus. In this year he made his attractive survey of properties in Lincolnshire, a comparatively small volume of 157 pages containing over 200 mini-maps (plates 41, 42), some of the holdings being very small[37]. For this he was paid £12 13s in the subsequent year.

For the next seven years there is no trace of Langdon in Oxford. It is possible that he still had the benefit of Cecil patronage, as we learn that he was at Exeter House in 1611 transcribing some Norfolk rentals originally made in 1592 for Sir Thomas[38]. A map of Newstead Waste made by him in 1613 is at Newstead Abbey[39]. He must have been at least intermittently resident at Tithby from 1603, the year in which handwriting believed to be his first occurs in the parish registers. No other maps of places in Nottinghamshire or adjoining counties attributable to Langdon have so far come to light.

In 1615 and 1616 Langdon was working for Corpus for the last time, in collaboration with a pupil, one Henry Wilcocke. The 26 maps in this series, for the most part of properties in Hampshire, are the subject of entries in the Liber Magnus for those years under the heading 'impensae e cista finium'. Langdon received a total of £40 18s 6d in the course of the two years. The payments to Wilcocke, less certain because some of the entries are confused, may be said to add up to £13 11s 10d[40].

Henry Wilcocke was apparently a beginner. The two men worked closely together. Three maps, all drawn in April 1615, are entitled 'by Henry Wilcocke with the help and direction of Thomas Langdon'. Later there are some 'drawne . . . by Tho. Langdon and Henry Wilcocke'. Yet others were drawn by Wilcocke alone (pl. 43). But nothing is heard of Henry Wilcocke after 1616, nor are there any indications that Langdon was employed by any of the Oxford colleges thereafter, though he was examined as to one of the All Souls maps of Whatborough in 1620[41].

Langdon's last assignment so far as at present known was for the London Charterhouse. On December 9 1616 the Governors resolved to have their estates 'in any the Countyes Lincolnshire, Cambridgeshire, Essex, Middlesex and Wiltes or els where' surveyed by 'a skilful Surveior'. This last phrase was struck out shortly after and the name 'Thomas Langdon Clerke' put in its place. Two years later it was decided that he should be paid 'the somme of twenty poundes ouer and aboue the monyes that haue bene already paid unto him for his great paines and charges that he hath bene att in surveyinge writing and making the books and plotts of the seuerall Mannors of Elcombe, Balsham and Campes'[42]. These entries clearly do not tell the whole story. Some maps of Castle Camps (partly fragmentary), made by Langdon in 1617 and 1618, survive. Others relating to Cambridgeshire and Wiltshire can be inferred; and copies made by John Prickett of Highgate in 1790–91 of eleven Cambridgeshire maps are still among the muniments[43]. The scope of Langdon's activities at Charterhouse remains in doubt, but it does not appear that he completed the comprehensive program originally intended by the Governors.

Langdon's son-in-law, George Darker, to whom he left his surveying instruments, may have entered the household as his assistant, but no evidence of surveys made by him has come to light. He married Rosamund Langdon by licence at St Peter's Nottingham 3 July 1630 and was then described as of Scalford Leicestershire, gent. Rosamund Darker was buried at Tithby 2 November 1633, their daughter Rosamund being baptized there the next day. From 1634–37 Darker was curate at Thurgarton Nottinghamshire. He then became rector of nearby Elston. About the same time, probably, he re-married: a son, George, was baptized there 29 September 1639. George Darker was buried at Elston in 1658[44].

Thus, in relative obscurity, ends the surveying tradition which can be traced back to Peter Kempe around a hundred years previously. The period enshrines what may be thought of as a golden age of estate cartography attaining its peak in the generation 1585–1615. To look for convincing explanations for this phenomenon may be thought premature. Clerke and Langdon are two names among scores, and other relevant biographies remain largely unresearched.

But it is perhaps not too early to begin to isolate factors in Tudor economy and Tudor society which may have been contributory. Among these should certainly be counted the fluid land market which developed after the Dissolution and which persisted up to the Restoration. This left plenty of room for doubts as to the extent of properties acquired by the new men, latent doubts which might emerge unexpectedly. The conflict between Lord Cromwell and All Souls in 1586 is paralleled by a boundary dispute at Broughton near Skipton in the same year, in which Christopher Saxton was nominated to survey. Both these cases involved commissions set up by the Court of Exchequer which had come to specialise in estate matters after it succeeded to the Court of Augmentations in 1544. The commissions had for object the investigation of facts on the spot, and mapping of the terrain could be a crucial part of the routine. At Old Byland in 1598, also mapped by Saxton, there was an explicit order by the Exchequer for the making of a 'perfect plott of the places and grounds mentioned' and this was to be 'at the equall chardge of both the said parties'[45].

This use of maps, for which there is no apparent precedent, should perhaps be viewed in the context of innovations characteristic of the equitable jurisdiction increasingly exercised by the central courts and their provincial analogues during the reign of Elizabeth. Among comparable developments were the displacement of oral evidence by written submissions and of Latin by the English language, even of obsolete specialised handwritings by the newfangled italic. These were practical reforms, and the map, which permitted court officials operating at a distance from the local contention to appreciate the terrain, falls easily into context.

The uncertainties inseparable from the rapid turnover of land were no doubt compounded by the readiness of landowners, many of whom were lawyers, to have recourse to law. It was not necessary to be litigious to get into court. A vexatious action could be launched out of the blue. The Fellows of All Souls, defending themselves from the royal onslaught on their Middlesex woods with the plea that these were an essential reserve, pointed out that 'if misfortun sholde befalle the College as fire ruin invasion or sutes in Lawe, our only refuge is the College woods'. Of these hazards 'sutes in Lawe' were certainly not the least. They had been 'of late and at this present are very chargeable and hereafter like to be rather more than lesse[46]'.

Corporations like All Souls seem to have been among the first to improve their defences. Prudence dictated that it was preferable to map estates comprehensively in advance rather than wait until an emergency compelled hasty action. Almost at the same time that the College embarked on their program, Christopher Saxton was surveying extensively for St Thomas's Hospital. The work was done between 1589 and 1593. These were clearly not *ad hoc* operations: at one point Saxton is revealingly instructed to measure the hospital's Kentish properties 'as his leysure will serve him'[47]. Possibly some of the rest of the fifty odd maps and measured terriers by the Saxtons were elements in a comprehensive record, but others look as though they were made in the context of an actual dispute. The courts never seem to be far away.[48]

It would be an over-simplification to conclude that litigation, or apprehensions about litigation, were the sole or even the dominant consideration. Apart from the mundane needs of day-to-day estate management, prestige was also involved. Robert Hovenden may well have been truthful in blaming the absence of maps at All Souls in 1587 on the parsimony of the Fellows. But, as already noticed, the high tables of Merton and New College, not so long afterwards, were taking a pride in their maps. They continued to be admired by some; Cole thought Langdon's originals 'very elegantly and masterly done'[49].

To judge by his will (apart from those tell-tale instruments), Thomas Langdon could easily be written off as an insignificant country parson, busying himself about his glebe, and fussing in old age about a watch he had almost forgotten lending. But he emerges as a man of impressive attainments: an academic of standing, qualified in an unusual legal specialism, with a still uncommon mathematical dexterity and abilities as a draughtsman transcending the repertoire of cartographic embellishment, witness his 'Typus Collegii[50]'. In this versatility, which was characteristically Elizabethan, he stands in contrast with Aaron Rathborne, his near contemporary. Rathborne, who may well have been technically Langdon's superior, published *The Surveyor* in 1616, a work in which the idea of the land surveyor is clearly differentiated from the Tudor omnium-gatherum official who combined the functions of land steward, lawyer, quantifier, architect and engineer Rathborne discarded the 'infinite other Conclusions Geometricall . . . for that they are without the scope and limits of Survey'; and insists that, though it is useful for a surveyor to have some legal knowledge, he must not pretend to be a lawyer. He should not even aspire to put his results into Latin 'considering that a reasonable surveyor may be lame of that legge'[51]. This was a blue print for the 'mechanic' of the future, without pretensions to gentility nor all-round education, but with the job at his fingertips. Presumably Langdon must have seen the book. One wonders if the two men ever met; and if they did what they made of one another.

Appendix 1

Will of Peter Kempe

(P.C.C. 1 Daughtry)

In the name of god Amen the seconde daie of December 1576. I Peter Kempe of Stamford in the countie of Lyncoln of perfect memory do [make – *cancelled*] pronownce this my last will as followeth First I bequeath my Sowle to almighty god I give to Peter Oxley the lease of my howse I dwell in Item I giue To Thomas Clarke twentie poundes Item I giue to Anne Hogham one of my white cuppes of siluer And I ordeyn Nicholas Wolrich and Richard Shutt my executours

witnesses   William Atkinson
William Hogham
Thomas Clerke

Appendix 2

Will of Thomas Clerke

(P.C.C. 66 Harrington)

In the name of god amen The eighteenth daie of Aprill anno domini Millesimo Quingen[tesi]mo Nonagesimo Secundo, and in the thirtie fourth yeere of the raigne of our soueraigne Ladie Elizabeth by the grace of god of Englande Fraunce and Irelande Queene defender of the faith &c I Thomas Clarcke of Stamforde St Martines in the countie of North[ampton] gent beinge in perfecte and sounde remembrance, (thanckes be to the everlivinge lorde thearefore) doe make and ordaine this my laste will and testamente in manner and forme followinge viz. Firste I bequeath my soule into the handes of god and his sonn Christe mine onlie Redemer and Sauiour by whose blud the same is washed from all his sinnes, and beinge as read as scarlett is become white as snowe, and by noe other meanes either papisticall or other Schimaticall [*ie* schismatical] devise, Beseechinge him for his mercies sake to receave the same, notwithstandinge the wretchedness I haue committed hath made the same the sincke of sinn, and pudle of perdition; Yeat o lorde save me for this mercies sake, and I commende my bodie to the earth from whence it came, and to be buried within the church of St Martines aforesaide, and soe neere the place whear my old master Peeter Kemp [er *cancelled*] lieth as maie be hopinge to rise againe with him and the residewe of the electe at the laste daie to gloriefie god, and to singe Osanna to the highest And whereas it hathe pleased god of his goodnes, far beyond the measure of my deserte to commit vnto me this small talente, for the which at the laste daie I must giue accompte I beseech him thearfore, that I maie dispose the same to his will, guided theare vnto by his worde, and that it maie please him to guide and blesse my purposes, and in his heavenlie wisdome to dispose the same, Soe that himselfe maie be glorified theareby, notwithstandinge that vaine man after his fonde and earthlie fashion doth vndertake to order the same; Yeat good lorde blesse the purposes of thie servaunte, and establish his deuises. Firste I giue to the poore people of St Martins Ten shillinges. And to the church of St Martins tenn shillinges towardes the repaire theareof wishinge the parishners theare better to respecte the vpholdinge the temple of the lorde whearein his worde is preached and his name glorified, leaste in his wrath he take yt awaie, and giue yt to others. Item I giue vnto my sonn William Clarke one hundreth marckes of lawefull englishe moneie to be paide him by my Exequutor when as he shall accomplishe the age of twentie and one yeeres. Item I giue vnto my daughter Ann Clarke one hundreth poundes of lawefull Englishe moneie to be paide her by my Exequutor, at the daie of her lawefull marriage or when as shee shall accomplishe the age of twentie yeeres. Item I giue [*insertion*: vnto] to [*sic*] my sonn Richarde one hundreth marckes of lawefull englishe moneie to be paide him by mine Exequutor when as he shall accomplishe the age of twentie one yeeres. Item I doe also giue vnto my daughter Elizabeth Clarke one hundreth poundes of lawefull englishe moneie, to be also paide her by my Exequutor at the daie of her lawefull marriage or as soone as shee shall accomplishe the age of twentie yeeres. And wheareas it hathe pleased my good and worshipfull master Sir Thomas Cecill knighte heeretofore to promise me a lease of the howse whearein I nowe doe dwell, I shall moste humblie desier him to continue that good purpose, and intencion to my poore wiefe and childrenn; And I doe giue him as a tokenn of my humble and dutifull good will my booke of plottes of all the seuerall sheires in Englande with Camdens discription[52] beseechinge him rather to accepte the good will of the giver then the gifte. Item I giue to master Richarde Shute my table of Dialogues betwine the philosopher and Justice Prouided allwaies and notwithstandinge my former devise concerninge the severall legacies before by me given vnto my childrenn, That if anie of them shall departe this liefe before theie shall accomplish their former ages; That then their partes and porcions shalbe equallie diuided amongste the others livinge, and paiable with their porcions [of *altered to* to] them before given Item I giue vnto euerie my men servantes dwellinge with me out of my goodes ouer and besides their wages twentie shillinges a peece: And vnto euerie woman servaunte tenn shillinges a peece. Item I giue vnto my aunte Inman of Stapleforthe to bestowe vppon my cozen Coningeworthe if she please five marckes of lawefull englishe moneie, To be paide vppon the laste paimente to me dewe by the lorde Barckley. Item I giue vnto master Reginald waters gent a gold hoope ringe as a tokenn of my good will. Item I giue vnto William Deane as a token also of my good will, and for his paines taken in writinge of this my will, tenn shillinges Item I doe giue vnto my lovinge servaunte Thomas Langden, all my bookes and instrumentes as well mathematicall as geometricall. Item I doe ordaine and nominate my lovinge and frendlie wief Ann Clarke my sole Exequutor of this my laste will and testamente vnto whome I doe giue all the residewe of my goodes cattells and chattells as well moueable as immoueable quick as dead nowe or heereafter in this will not disposed. And I doe ordaine and make Supervisers of this my saide will my lovinge brotherne in lawe Thomas Dandie gent, and William Odell gent whom I hartelie praie to take the charge vppon them, and vnto whom my will and pleasure is to referr the orderinge and managinge of this my saide will to the effecte aforesaide. And also [*insertion*: hereafter] to determin anie matter quarrell or contencion whatsoeuer that maie happenn to arise or growe by meanes of this my saide will or anie parte theareof or to anie person or persons thearein mencioned and named, with this especiall prouiso, that if anie person or persons before named doe refuse to stande to or to abide their awardes rule and judgemente That then this my presente gifte and bequest before mencioned to anie suche person or personns to be vtterlie voide notwithstandinge anie thinge thearin before contained. And I will that the same shalbe and remaine to the vses of the reste of my childrenn in equall proporcions as is aforesaide And in liewe of this paines and care the which after this bolde manner I doe impose vppon theis gentlmen, whose frindeship in my liefe I allwaies founde firme, I doe giue vnto either of them a spurr Riall as a token of my good will. Item I doe giue vnto master Atherton in respecte of his frindship to me allwaies shewed tenn shillinges. Item I forgiue poore Stringer the debtes that he owethe me. Item I giue to my Cosen Stephenn Barnewell and his wiefe each of them a golde ringe. Also I bequeath to master Jeffrie Baker alias Harrop Robert Reuell and Aquila Cooke each a paire of gilte walsingeham gloves to the value of fortie pence a peece. Item I giue my sister Dandie a gennuy of golde. Also I giue to master Doctor a paire of silke stockinges. And also I giue to all my wives sister Alyue each of them a gennuy of golde by the discrecion of mine Exequutrix. Tho: Clerke. thea[?r] beinge witnesses Thomas Atherton. Aquila Cooke and William Deane notarie.

Appendix 3

Will of Thomas Langdon

(Southwell Diocesan Record Office)

In the name of god Amen the first day of march in the thirtenth yeare of the raigne of our soueraigne lord Charles by the grace of god of England Skotland France and Ireland kinge defender of the faith &c I Thomas Langdon of Tithby in the county of Nottingham Clarke revokeinge all former wills, I being nowe though though [*sic*] weak in body yet of perfect remembrance (thanckes be to god therefore) doe make this my last will in maner and forme following that is to say, First I bequeath my soule into the handes of almighty god my maker and of Jhesu christ myn only saviour and my body to be buryed in the chancell of Tithbye or els where at the discretion of myne executrix Item I geve towardes the repair of the church of Tithbye aforesaid tenne shillinges. Item I gev to the poorest [*erasure*: of Tithby] of Tithbye, that is to say to william Clarke, John pecke and henry Chadwicke to every of them two shilinges six pence, and to George Emerson and Alice his wife to either of them iis vid. Item I geve to the poore of Cropwell butler ten shillinges to be distributed at the discreation of myne executrix Item [*erasure*: I geve to my kinsman Thomas Langdon dwelling in the George yard at Lambeth thirty poundes to be payd in maner and forme followeing that is to saye ten poundes within twelve monethes after my decease and the other twenty poundes I will shalbe paid at the decease of Johan my wife]. Item I geve to my Sister Pachet and to Thomas Pachet to either of them five shillings. Item I geve to my servantes that shalbe with me at my death to everye of them iis vid. [*erasure*: Item I geve to Rosamund darker my grandchild over and besides the hundred and fifty poundes to be repayd her by my brother darker, Thirtye poundes to bepaid her at the age of eighteene yeares]. Lasly I doe ordayne constitute and apointe my loving wife Johan Langdon (1) the sole executrix of this my last will and testam[en]t to whom I geve all the residue of my goodes unbequeathed my debtes and Legacies being paid and funerall charges discharged to whom [*insertion*: also] I comitt the tuition and education of my said grandchilde [*erasure*: and the use of her portion untill shee shall atteine vnto her said age of eighteene yeares] Lastly I gev to my son George darker all my Surveying instrum(en)ts in witnes whereof I have hereunto set my hand and seale the day and yeare first above written.

Tho. Langdon.

In the presence of   Robert Shipman (1)   Roger Marshall (1)   George bell
                                                his marke   his marke

further [*erasure*: the] my will is that whereas my kinsman Tho. langdon hath a wach [*erasure*: ?man] of myne which he hath witholden long [*erasure*: if] if he [*erasure of four or five letters*] doe return it safe I do gev unto him xxs & and [*sic*] one Cowe good and yong & six sheepe. if he doe not retorne the wach safe my will is he shall have onely xxs which I geve for the vse of his son John Langdon. Exhorting my said executrix As god shall bless her in estat to consider him further whengod shall her [*sic*]. but especeally our grandchild Rosam[un]d Darker to whom she is bound in in [*sic*] natur as well as my selfe.

(1) *marked* iurat'   Tho. Langdon

1. The wills are printed as Appendices 1, 2 and 3. Readers may find the narrative easier to follow if they study them before proceeding further. I am especially grateful to Paul Rutledgefor checking my transcripts.

2. B.W. Beckingsale, *Burghley, Tudor Statesman, 1520–1598* (London, 1967), ch xvii.

3. Hatfield House, Cecil Papers, vol. 140, f. 30. My thanks are due to the Marquess of Salisbury for access to his muniments, and to his Librarian and Archivist, Robin Harcourt Williams, for help and advice; to the late Marquess of Exeter; to Viscount Coke; to the Warden and Fellows of All Souls College, the Principal and Fellows of Brasenose College, the President and Fellows of Corpus Christi College (Oxford), the Warden and Fellows of Merton College, and to the Warden and Fellows of New College; to the Master and Governors of Sutton's Hospital, and to their Registrar and Clerk; to staff at the British Library, particularly to Sarah Tyacke and Peter Barber; to John Simmons for guidance, and a deal of hospitality at All Souls, and the like to Roger Highfield at Merton; to Christopher Woolgar at Corpus; to W.O. Hassall for encouragement and expertise unstintingly deployed; to archivists and staff at a number of record offices, notably at Norfolk, Northampton, Nottingham and Ipswich, and at the 5 Oxford colleges; and to friends, relatives and colleagues who lent an eye or an ear, made suggestions, or assisted practically.

4. BL Cotton MS Titus B.IV., f. 111. *A Collection in English of the Statutes now in force* (London, 1594), f. 439v., see 'Surueiours'.

5. For the most up-to-date account of Saxton's relations with Seckford and Cecil see Ifor M. Evans and Heather Lawrence, *Christopher Saxton, Elizabethan Map-Maker* (Wakefield, 1979), ch. 1 and *passim*.

6. Reproduced in Sarah Tyacke and John Huddy, *Christopher Saxton and Tudor map-making* (London, 1980), p. 26.

7. Hatfield House, Cecil Papers, Maps Supp. 27.

8. Exeter MS 57/7.

9. From Exeter MS 49/7 it would appear that Cecil acquired the Fleur-de-Luce in the Strand in 1561. Agas subsequently used it as a London address.

10. BL Lansdowne MS 84, f. 32.

11. Richard C. Barnett, *Place, Profit and Power: A Study of the Servants of William Cecil, Elizabethan Statesman* (University of North Carolina, 1969).

12. Barnett, pp. 91–94 and pp. 123–127.

13. Hatfield House, Cecil Papers, vol. 140, f. 20.

14. Holkham Hall, Norfolk, Holkham Maps, under re-classification.

15. Parish of St Martin, Stamford, Register of Births.

16. M.W. Beresford, *History on the Ground* (London, 1957), pp. 116–123.

17. This map, now framed and glazed, is dated 1586; cf.All Souls College, Hovenden Maps, vol. 1 No. 19, also of 1586; the third version, undated and unascribed, is listed by Charles Trice Martin, *Catalogue of the Archives in the Muniment Rooms of All Souls' College* (London, 1877), p. 269 as Whadborough 219.

18. All Souls College, Oxford, Hovenden Maps, vol. III, Nos. 8–12.

19. The Computus Rolls are listed by Trice Martin p. 405.

20. For a detailed account of this episode (but with significant gaps in the documentation) 'All Souls v. Lady Jane Stafford' in *Collectanea* edited by C.R.L. Fletcher. (Oxford, 1885–.), IV; BL Lansdowne MS 54, 16, 18, 22 and 30. The College was ultimately successful in beating off Lady Jane.

21. BL Add MS 6197, f. 15 sqq.

22. The particulars of this marriage as given in Oswald Barron, *Northamptonshire Families* (Victoria County History *Northants*, Genealogical Volume, London, 1906), are at variance with J.W. Burgon, *The Life and Times of Sir Thomas Gresham* (London, 1839) I, 49–52 and II, 491.

23. PRO SP 46/18, f. 23.

24. Suffolk Record Office (Ipswich Branch) HB 11: 590/III/7; cf. W.A. Copinger, *The Manors of Suffolk* (London, 1905) II, 270. The sales of Westacre Norfolk, described by Lawrence Stone in *An Elizabethan: Sir Horatio Palavicino* (Oxford, 1956) pp. 270–271, may be a related transaction.

25. Holkham Hall Norfolk, Holkham Maps, under re-classification. There is a long account of the dispute in Holkham MSS, Wighton Deeds 103; Wighton Deeds 115 is a summary made about a decade later.

26. The vagaries of college accounting make it difficult to be sure that all relevant entries have been traced. At All Souls for the period 1580–1609 there are normally two versions of each annual roll, one on paper and one on parchment.There are occasionally discrepancies between the two and a few rolls are missing. Expenditure on estate surveying was found under the headings 'variae expensae' and 'summa equitantium', and only these were systematically searched. Expenditure could be recorded elsewhere if no funds were available in the account normally used (see Peter Eden, 'Land Surveyors in Norfolk, 1550–1850' (part 1) *Norfolk Archaeology*, 35 (1977), iv, and pp. 477–478 and (f. 31).

27. Parish of St Martin, Stamford, Register of Burials.

28. Norfolk Record Office, Anthony Norris's Collection (Rye MS 4 and 5), 1. p. 363.

29. Oxford University Archives, Register of Congregation and Convocation 1595-1606, f. 67 and f. 80.

30. PRO SP 46/19, f. 68.

31. Norfolk Record Office BIR/25.

32. No corresponding maps are held at All Souls.

33. F.W. Steer, *The Archives of New College, Oxford: a Catalogue* (Chichester, 1974), nos. 2375, 4466 and 5672.

34. Liber Rationarius Bursarium Coll. Mert. 1 (1585–1633), f. 85; Coll. Mert. Registrum 1567–1731, f. 206 v.

35. Merton College Records 6.17 and 6.19; BL Add. MS 5823, ff. 148v.–155v.

36. Corpus Christi College Oxford, Maps 2, 7, 53, 64, 65 and 154. The Liber Magnus of the College contains the bursarial accounts, and payments were found under the headings 'impensae equitantium', 'impensae placitorum' and 'impensae e cista finium'; other headings were not systematically searched (see fn. 26 above).

37. Corpus Christi College Oxford, Records, in Da 5.

38. Holkham Hall Norfolk, Holkham MSS, Castle Acre Deeds 60.

39. A tracing (M 7636) is at the Nottinghamshire Record Office.

40. Corpus Christi College Oxford, Records, Mc. 3.

41. All Souls College Oxford, Hovenden Maps, Vol. 1 No. 19, endorsement.

42. Charterhouse Muniments, Minute Book A, pp. 66 and 126.

43. Charterhouse Muniments MP 2/22. The copies by John Prickett are in a bound volume with other maps of similar date.There were at least two successive John Pricketts and it is not known which is the copyist – see Peter Eden, *Dictionary of Land Surveyors and Local*

Cartographers of Great Britain and Ireland 1550–1850 (Folkestone, 1979), entry P 333.

44. Parishes of Elston, Thurgarton and Tithby Nottinghamshire, Registers (at County Record Office); information Nottinghamshire Record Office.
45. Beresford, p. 55.
46. BL Landsdowne MS 54.30.
47. Evans and Lawrence p. 82.
48. Evans and Lawrence chs. 8 and 9.

49. BL Add. MS 5823 f. 148v.
50. The Typus Collegii is a bird's-eye view of the College of All Souls from the South-east drawn by Langdon *c*1600, perhaps as a frontispiece to the Hovenden Maps.
51. Aaron Rathborne, *The Surveyor in Foure bookes* (London, 1616), p. 173, p. 175 and p. 218.
52. The precise nature of Clerke's bequests to Sir Thomas Cecil will probably remain an unresolved mystery.

John Schofield

Ralph Treswell's surveys of London houses *c*1612

The Great Fire of London in 1666 swept away more than two-thirds of the medieval city, and this cataclysmic removal of most of the evidence has constantly hampered students of London's pre-Fire buildings. But in recent years, prompted largely by increased provision for archaeological and documentary investigation of development sites in the City, the sources for reconstruction of the medieval and post-medieval townscape are being re-examined. There are a small number of buildings in the City and immediately outside which date from the medieval period: the Guildhall itself (1430) and Merchant Taylors' Hall (fifteenth century), both restored after war damage, are the best known examples. In the area in the north-east of the city not devastated by the Great Fire, many medieval buildings survived in altered forms to be sketched or planned by modern antiquaries before they disappeared in the nineteenth century. Since 1973 the Museum of London has excavated many medieval sites in its rescue programme, particularly along the waterfront.

London also possesses a wealth of documentary evidence from the mid-thirteenth century: building regulations, records of courts, inquisitions and the central registry of deeds and wills (the Husting Rolls). The livery companies, through the piety and generosity of their members, became by 1540 administrators of large amounts of property. In many cases the history of a specific property can be reconstructed by correlation of the official records with deeds, wills and views (when the properties were inspected for repairs by a company official) kept by the company.

The Dissolution of the monasteries released a great amount of London land on to the property market: not only the precincts of the conventual houses themselves, but their much larger holdings of property in the city and elsewhere. By the late-sixteenth century some of this ex-monastic property was being passed, by donation or bequest, to charitable institutions – predominantly the livery companies, but also the reformed hospitals of Edward VI's foundation. Where sixteenth century company records survive, the increase in the property portfolio and the amount of land management business this generated can be easily discerned. One of the developments of the time seems to have been the wider use of the bird's-eye-view, lease plan or map, a vital document when the institution's lands might be several days' ride from the estate office. In the City of London the surveyor's problem was very different. Here blocks of property varied in size from one to thirty tenancies, in buildings up to five storeys high. On upper floors, rooms often pushed into and over adjacent tenancies of the same landlord. Accurate records of the dimensions of rooms were critical, for space was at a premium. The city was experiencing a population explosion, and the surveyor had to keep control of an unprecedented amount of information about buildings which, despite civic regulations to the contrary, were expanding upwards and outwards at alarming speed.

To our great good fortune, the surveys of two institutional portfolios of property in London, including Southwark and Westminster, survive from the early seventeenth century. They are the work of Ralph Treswell the elder, engaged by the Clothworkers' Company in 1612 and Christ's Hospital, the city's orphanage, in 1612–13. Treswell was a member of the Painter-Stainers' Company, being one of the trustees to whom the company hall was granted in 1580; the group granted it to another in 1605[1]. A Raffe Treswell, painter, was paid £8 10s by the Carpenters' Company in 1567–8 for painting three streamers and a banner[2]; if this is the Treswell of the present study, he must have been approaching 80 when he died in or shortly after 1616. Perhaps Treswell brought to the art of the measured survey his special talents as a painter of streamers and banners, for his work blends careful transcription and accuracy with considerable artistic grace.

Treswell's work for the Clothworkers' Company in 1612, apparently transcribed by him into a Planbook, has been partly published[3]. It comprises thirty water-colour plans of the Company's property in the city. The great majority of the plans have accompanying texts of reference which describe, with measurements, the upper storeys of each building. A second collection of nineteen pages of plans in the Evidence Book of Christ's Hospital (Guildhall MS 12,805) has, apart from one untypical drawing, never been published. The present paper sets out to describe this second collection and then assess the information in both planbooks for the student of post-medieval building and urban topography.

The Evidence Book of Christ's Hospital is a manuscript volume of about 500 pages in a sixteenth century binding. The first 25 pages are occupied by an incomplete rental of Hospital property in London and the surrounding counties; thereafter most of the book is blank. Bound near the end of the book is an inserted section of paper folios; nineteen pages of plans, ranging from single houses grouped three to a page to blocks of property drawn across a double-page, preceded by three late seventeenth century plans of three of the same properties. The plans of the larger group are clearly the work of Ralph Treswell the elder, who signed and dated one of the double-page plans to 1610. Treswell is recorded as a governor of Christ's Hospital between his appointment in July 1603 and July 1616[4]. On 17 December 1612 the Court ordered that 'there shall be a fair book made of parchment wherein shall be entered a note of all the evidences concerning the lands and annuities belonging to this house[5]. The Evidence Book is a blank book of paper; evidently more thrifty counsels prevailed. The first page of the opening rental states that the purpose was to record the donors of property or bequests out of which property had been bought by the Hospital; and that this was done in the time of Mr Cogan, the treasurer. The date of Cogan's appointment, 1594, is placed in the margin of the opening statement. Cogan was replaced as treasurer in 1614[6]. The date of transcription of the plans for the Evidence Book can therefore be suggested as very late 1612 or 1613. They were first drawn and coloured on the folios and then bound in, probably by removing a section of the original pages. The three late-seventeenth century plans which precede them could have been transcribed into the existing book, for they all occupy single pages and do not display any sign of being drawn before the binding took place.

Other evidence suggests that the plans, in their original form, were drawn to accompany leases of 1607–11. In all but one case the names of tenants are inserted in the rooms they occupy (pl. 44). This was of course very necessary, since a much sub-divided block of property could contain up to a dozen tenancies. Deeds relating to the properties have been preserved and are now, in their original bundles, also in the Guildhall Library. Attached to three leases are further copies of three of the plans. In two of these cases, cited as 'the plot hereunto annexed', there is an attached lease plan, executed in a plain brown ink and wash; both are dated by the names of the lessees to 1607. The one dated plan in the Evidence Book is of 1610; circumstantial evidence would date two other plans to after 1608 and 1611. The use of colours, conventions and style are identical to the plans in the Clothworkers' planbook, a similar venture of 1612, for which Treswell was paid[7]. Unfortunately there is no record of any payment for the Christ's Hospital surveys; perhaps Treswell, being a governor, waived any fee. It seems therefore that Treswell may have been engaged on drawing up lease plans for Christ's Hospital from at least 1607, and that at the Court's request he transcribed the plans of the London property, which could be presented in the confines of a large book, into the Evidence Book in 1612/13. Although the incomplete rental at the front of the book stops half way through the Hospital's rural holdings, and we know that Treswell surveyed some of them for the Hospital from at least 1597, they were (and are) clearly too large in surveyed form to fit in such a book.

The Hospital plans are accompanied in fourteen of the twenty-one holdings by a text of reference describing, with measurements, the upper chambers of each building, preceded by a list of the ground floor rooms, 'as in the plot appeareth'. In a fifteenth case the measurements are written on the plan itself. These texts are being edited for forthcoming publication with the plans[8], so that the full value of Treswell's work may be more widely known.

Together, the two collections feature forty-nine blocks of London property surveyed in the opening decade of the seventeenth century. When used with the groundplans, the texts can provide information on the use of rooms, relative plot ratio (the total amount of floor-area divided by the site area – a measure of vertical density), the number of rooms in each tenancy, the proportion which were heated, and the proportions of groundspace either cellared or covered by buildings. They may help identify the medieval cores, where they existed, of these predominantly late-sixteenth century and early-seventeenth century buildings.

The majority of the plans in both planbooks are groundplans of individual buildings, or groups of contiguous buildings, with doorways, stairs and chimneys shown, along with yards and gardens. Nearly all the walls are coloured grey, and most are less than a foot thick, presumably indicating timber framing. Occasionally thicker walls, evidently of stone (in one case in the Clothworkers' planbook, the city wall), and sometimes so labelled, are shown (pl. 44); unfortunately the same colour is used as for the timber walls. Chimneys, walls and some further walls, nearly always surrounding gardens, are coloured bright red and were presumably of brick.

Study of the upper storey descriptions indicates that in many cases chimneys started on the first floor and were carried up as many as three further storeys (the majority of the Abchurch Lane houses in pl. 45). Such large stacks must have been supported down to the ground, either by masonry walls (which are not shown) or by corbelling out or coving under the first floor hearth, as in the case in the kitchen block of the still surviving Hoop and Grapes, Aldgate, of the mid-seventeenth century. It is also possible that Treswell drew party walls as of a conventional thickness except in unusual circumstances, such as two walls back to back; by London law, property boundaries were down the middle of party walls. The general distinction, however, between thin and thick walls when they are shown suggests that Treswell was in fact accurately surveying buildings almost totally timber-framed, and that by their sheer size the two collections of buildings represent a pre-Fire city in which houses of brick and stone were a rarity.

Three general types of post-medieval house can be seen in the plans. The large medieval courtyard house, adapted, rebuilt with more chambers and divided into tenancies, is found twice in the Clothworkers' and once in the Christ's Hospital books. The example from the Clothworkers' collection, redrawn for publication here (pl. 45) shows Foxe's Court, Nicholas Lane, entered through a three-storey street range. The house comprised a hall upon a cellar, entered by steps; the original hall appears to have been subdivided to provide a parlour. On the other side of the original screens passage was a kitchen with an enormous stack which occupied nearly all the end of the building. The gatehouse range to the lane had a first and second floor gallery on the court side, with access down to the court; each floor had several rooms the width of the range, as in galleried inns. Deeds in the Company's possession enable the property's history from 1363 to be outlined, though virtually nothing of the structural history is forthcoming. The large house and its associated smaller properties along Abchurch Lane were leased to John Basse, draper, in 1390. Thereafter drapers or shearmen are sporadically associated with it culminating in its ownership in 1520 by Oliver Claymond, the first master of the Clothworkers Company (formed by a union of shearmen and fullers in 1528). By his will of 1540 it passed to the Company.

The five houses to the bottom right hand (north-west) of the plan, in Abchurch Lane, were probably those built on the site by John Basse just before 1390; they are examples of the second and much more numerous type of house. This has two rooms in plan, on two, three or four floors, its narrow end to the street, and is well known from archaeological and documentary evidence in London from the early fourteenth century; the surviving Hoop and Grapes is a seventeenth century descendant. In these houses the ground floor is a shop or tavern, often with the two rooms thrown together to form one, and the hall of the tenant is on the first floor at the front, overlooking the street. In the Abchurch Lane examples, possibly because they were of the old medieval form, the kitchen is a separate building; but in the majority of the buildings surveyed by Treswell the kitchen occupies the back room on the first floor. Above were chambers and garrets; many of the rooms, including some of the garrets, were heated.

Houses only one room in extent are found both on principal streets, where they formed a screen for larger houses behind (pl. 46), and in courtyards where they assumed awkward, angular shapes to take up every inch of space. On principal streets they could reach five and a half storeys in height. The row of small dwellings along Billiter Lane, shown in plate 46, was composed in 1612 of buildings of various dates; most of the row had been rebuilt in stages since Company records began in 1528, and the specific building accounts survive.

Apart from showing ordinary houses of various sizes, the plans are valuable in providing examples of specialised buildings. There are taverns, inns with extensive stables, two company halls (of the Clothworkers and the Woodmongers) and a row of cook shops at Smithfield known as Pie Corner. Each collection has one set of almshouses; those at Whitefriars bequeathed to the Clothworkers by the Countess of Kent in 1540, and a group built at St Peter's Hill by David Smith, embroiderer to Elizabeth I, in 1576 and bequeathed to Christ's Hospital. The Clothworkers' collection includes two waterfront properties, one of which probably includes dyehouses. The Christ's Hospital estate at Westminster included land on three sides of the Woolstaple, apparently a market-hall building on twelve posts.

Many of the properties can be traced back to ecclesiastical owners before the Dissolution and the Reformation. Pending final study of the Clothworkers' deeds, which is in progress, it does seem that this is more the case with Christ's Hospital bequests, which were mostly made in the thirty years immediately preceding Treswell's survey. Evidently the character of the Clothworkers' portfolio was slightly different, being based on the accumulated estates of several prominent clothworkers in the early sixteenth century. Of the Christ's Hospital properties, only nine of the twenty-one blocks are *not* at present associated with former ecclesiastical owners, and in some cases this may only be because of lack of documentation before the 1540's. It can be suggested that this lack is more likely to be due to ecclesiastical ownership, since such properties, once acquired by the institutional landlord, would not be the subject of deeds enrolled on the Husting Rolls. The various types of religious landlord – Holy Trinity Priory, Aldgate; provincial monastic houses; parish fraternities and chantry bequests are all represented. Thus the deeds and their plans illustrate both the sources of the property acquired, through bequest or purchase, by two of the new type of institutional landlord, hospitals and livery companies, in the sixteenth century; and the post-medieval histories of a selection of monastic and parish properties.

The value of Treswell's work must now be assessed by topographers, historians, archaeologists and students of vernacular architecture. The present author is engaged upon study of the plans as illustrations of the history and development of the different house-forms in pre-Fire London. The corpus of buildings provided by Treswell is a complement to the views on Elizabethan London given by our other principal source, John Stow in his *Survey* of 1598. Stow bemoaned the population explosion of his time and the mean dwellings which sprouted everywhere to contain it; he remembered the 'arched gates' and grand halls of his youth. He looks back with envy at the pre-Dissolution times. Here, in the work of Ralph Treswell, are some of the 'mean dwellings'; here is the day-to-day surveyor measuring timber walls, chimneys, stairs and privies. He investigates and records the smallest alley and backyard. Our view of London around 1600 is corrected, and the buildings of pre-Fire London begin to take shape.

Appendix

The text of reference for the houses in plate 44, with interim analysis; an example from the Christ's Hospital plan book. Unfortunately this particular example illustrates a variety of features of the drawings, but is short on tenurial history. The text has been condensed from the original; the ground floor description has been omitted, and numbers in brackets refer to (inferred) storeys above the ground.

21–2 Trinity Lane (formerly Knightrider Street)

William Mascall, mercer, by his will of 11 September 1608 gave £160 to Christ's Hospital, out of which the hospital appears to have bought the two properties shown in a Treswell plan, though no deeds showing the actual investment of the money survive. These houses were however in the possession of the hospital in 1605, before the gift, and it is possible that the governors 'decided to appropriate them as an investment of Mascall's gift, or rather as a security for performance of his intention'[9].

The houses in the plan are 3½ storeys high. Abraham Fryth's drinking rooms are an intriguing puzzle. On the first floor part of the upper chamber floor was open to light the ground floor room – presumably some kind of gallery. A distinction is made between the stone wall which was the west side of the building and the 'paper wall' which divided Fryth from Welshow's long, narrow tenancy. It seems possible that the stone walls shown are the relics of a large medieval house with a cellar which was later partitioned to reflect the creation of Welshaw's tenancy. It is noteworthy that the Jarret's Hall to the north west, to which a garret on the boundary is supposed to belong, was Gerard's Hall, Basing Lane, with its splendid late-thirteenth century undercroft (destroyed in 1852).

Text of reference, Evidence Book:

Abraham Fryth: (2) A chamber or room with a chimney 19½' long besides the stone wall on the W side which is 2' thick and the paper wall wall on the E side and part of this room is open on the floor to give light; One other room with a chimney and the funnel of the kitchen chimney 20' × 13' with a house of office 6' × 3' at the one end and ×4' at the other with a shed next the same 8' × 7'; (3) A chamber with a chimney 14' × 12' with a study 7' × 3½', some part lying on the stone wall next the gate, one other chamber with a chimney besides the passage 14½' × 12½', one other chamber with a chimney 11½' × 11'; (4) A garret with a chimney 19½' × 12', a garret next the street 14½' × 13½' and [a garret?] 20½' × 13½'; A cellar N-S 49½' × 17½' at the S end × 25½' at the N end with a corner.

Thomas Alcoke: (2) A hall with stairs and chimney 14½' × 14½', one other room next the hall 16' × 8', with the chimney, stairs and study; (3) One other chamber over the hall 16' with stairs × 14½' with a chimney; (4) One garret above all 16' × 14'; Also a cellar 11½' × 10'.

Thomas Alcocke in the occupation of George Eakines: (2) A hall over the shop 16' with chimney and stairs × 14½', one other chamber 12½' × 8', a kitchen with a chimney 15½' × 8'; (3) One other chamber over the chamber over the chamber before [sic] 16½' with stairs and chimney × 15½'; (4) A garret over the chamber before 16' × 15'; Also a cellar under the shop with a trap door 14½' × 11½', with a little nook under the stairs.

Robert Rowse: (2) A hall over the shop 15½' with stairs and chimney × 14½', one other room with a funnel of a privy out of the room above 15½' × 10½', a kitchen on the S side with stairs into the garret 15½' on the E side to the stone wall 13½' on the N side 15½'; (3) A garret over his house divided into several partitions with a stone wall.

Thomas Chilton: (2) A chamber the W side in l. with two pairs of stairs 17' besides the chimney, and in b. on the S side, E and W in part 8', one other chamber over West's shop 11' × 10½' with stairs up; (3) A chamber over the other with chimney and stairs 19' × 11½', at the N end of the chamber 8½', then on the E side 6½', the turning 2½', the rest of the E side 11½', this room hath a privy in it; (4) a garret 19½' × 11½', also a chamber over his hall 16½' × 11½', then a little room over Rowse's hall 8½' × 5'.

Thomas Alcock in the occupation of West: (2) A chamber over Frythe's kitchen bredth with stairs and chimney 14½' × 11½', a chamber 20' × in b. at the W end 7' 9" with a chimney; (3) Two garrets with stairs and chimney 26' × 12', also at the NW corner of one of these garrets is a corner 5' one way and 7' another way being no part of this house but supposed to be of Jarrards Hall; A cellar under the shop with a privy in it 14½' × 7'.

John Welshaw: (2) A chamber 12½' × 9½' with a chimney and stairs, a chamber or a kitchen with a chimney 15' × 8' 3", a chamber 8½' × 8½', note that all the E side of this house standeth on a stone wall, next to a stone wall belonging to the said parish (Holy Trinity the Less); ?(3) a chamber next the street with chimney and study 14½' × 12½', a chamber 12' × 8'; ?(4) a chamber 12' long, at the S end 7' 10", at the N end 5½'; ?(5) a garret next the street 14½' × 11½', a garret 8½' × 15½'.

1. Guildhall Library MS 5670.

2. *Records of the Worshipful Company of Carpenters; Volume IV Wardens Accounts 1546–71*, edited by B. Marsh (London, 1916), p. 208.

3. London Topographical Society Publication no. LXXII (1938), LXXIII (1939); 'The Clothworkers' Company: Book of Plans of the Company's Property made in 1612', *London Topographical Record* 18 (1942), 51–97. R. Weinstein, 'Clothworkers in St Stephen Coleman Parish, 1612', *London Topographical Record*, 24 (1980), 61–80.

4. Christ's Hospital Court Minute Book, Guildhall Library MS 12, 806/3, 68, 188.

5. Guildhall Library MS 12, 806/3, 146.

6. Guildhall Library MS 12, 806/3, 174.

7. Clothworkers' Company Court Orders 1605-23, f. 102v.

8. J. Schofield, 'An Early Seventeenth Century Collection of London House Plans', (forthcoming).

9. Charity Commissions, *Report* vol. 32, Part VI (London, 1840), p. 109.

G.L'E. Turner

Mathematical instrument-making in London in the sixteenth century

From about 1500, increased wealth and an enlarged population in England, as well as growing overseas trade, caused the profession of surveyor to develop markedly. Land surveying is an intensely practical activity, closely related to social conditions and demands. Following the dissolution of the monasteries in 1539, a large number of new estates were created, which helped to bring about the need for greater accuracy of measurement. Surveying textbooks at the beginning of the sixteenth century did not deal with accurate land measurement (geometrical surveying). *The Boke of Surveying and Improvements*, published in 1523 by John Fitzherbert,[1] contained chapter headings like this:

Howe many acres of medowe are of the demeyns and howe moche every acre is worthe and to what maner of catell it is moost necessary unto and howe many beestes it wyll fynde and what the pasture of a beest is worthe by the yere. [Chap. 3]

It was a textbook on carrying out audits or valuations, with nothing about map-making or land measurement. This tradition continued through the century, for Valentine Leigh, in 1577, covered much the same ground in *The Moste Profitable and commendable science, of Surueying of Landes, Tenementes, and Hereditamentes*. Leigh, however, did provide tables for estimating areas of land, and described 'The most excellent Rule for measuryng Wood Lande and other pieces of Lande, that are deformed or on all sides unequall' (Sig. P iv), by the use of simple diagrams, triangular or rectangular. Here Leigh had copied the scheme of Richard Benese, whose book on land measurement, published in 1537, is said to be only the second book on surveying in English.[2] Rough measurements were to be made with a wooden rod the length of a perch (16½ ft), and a cord of five perches in length.

But before the new, angular measuring techniques could be satisfactorily imported from the Continent during the second half of the century, a prior requirement was a knowledge of arithmetic. An important step was for arabic numerals to replace the roman. In the Exchequer Records arabic numerals were first used at the end of the sixteenth century, and roman did not entirely disappear in this stronghold of tradition until the mid-seventeenth century.[3] Accounts were done by using ruled boards or cloths, and casting-counters known as jettons.[4] Pen-reckoning was to be very necessary for the new breed of land surveyor, and the first text to help him was an anonymous work, *An Introduction for to learne to Recken with the Pen or work the Counters* (1537).[5] This was soon followed by the highly influential work of Robert Recorde (c1510–1558), whose *The Ground of Artes Teaching the Worke and practise of Arithmetike* was published in London in 1543, and ran through 28 editions to 1699.[6]

Recorde may be regarded as the founder of English mathematics, since his 'text-books in English opened the way to self-education for the new class of technicians'.[7] More than this, he was the founder of the English school of mathematical practitioners, among whom were later numbered many of the great London instrument-makers, since 'a generation of English scientists, especially non-university men, stated that Recorde's books had been their first tutors in the mathematical sciences'.[8]

The printer of *The Ground of Artes*, Reynor Wolfe, had not long left his native Drenthe, a province in the north of the Netherlands, to settle in London in 1533: even fifty years later, it was still difficult to find 'an English printer who could set up a mathematical work correctly'.[9] Throughout the sixteenth century the English were indebted to the Continent, and especially to the Netherlands, north and south, for the skills of printing, of engraving book illustrations, maps and instruments (often the work of the same craftsman), and for surveying techniques.

Another pioneer in the provision of textbooks and English translations of Continental practice was John Dee (1527–1608). A mathematical genius, he was a founder Fellow of Trinity College, Cambridge, in 1546. During the years 1547 to 1550 he visited Paris, Brussels and Louvain, studying mathematical practice, including the design and making of instruments for surveying, navigation, cartography, gunnery and dialling.[10] During this period abroad he worked with Gemma Frisius (1508–1555) and Gerard Mercator (1512–1594). Dee was singularly influential with his *Preface* (1570), written for the first English translation of Euclid by Henry Billingsley (d 1606).[11] Here Dee tabulated and discussed systematically all the practical applications of arithmetic and geometry, in the same manner as Petrus Rames (Pierre de la Ramée) (1515–1572), of Paris.[12]

A recent detailed study by Dr John Roche has traced the history of the astronomer's cross staff from Levi ben Gerson (1288–1344) to Gemma Frisius, who published in 1545 'the most extensive book ever written on the cross staff'.[13] Gemma described an instrument intended to serve as a hand-held astronomer's staff, as a surveyor's staff, and as a navigator's staff. As a surveying instrument, it could measure heights of buildings with no calculation, and, for the relatively untutored, could serve in a triangulation survey.[14]

In 1547 Dee brought home with him from Louvain such a staff, devised by Gemma Frisius, but perhaps actually made by Gerard Mercator. Dr Roche points out the interesting fact that this is the earliest reference so far discovered to an *actual* astronomer's or surveyor's cross staff in any English list of instruments.[15] An example of this type of staff, made in 1571 by the nephew of Gemma, is in the British Museum.[16]

As further confirmation of the influence of the Low Countries in bringing printing, engraving, and surveying to England, Christopher Saxton's *An Atlas of England and Wales*, published in London in 1579, contains 34 maps, 23 of them bearing the engraver's name. There are seven different signatures, four of them by Flemings, three by Englishmen. The Flemish names are: Remigius Hogenberg (on 9 maps); Lenaert Terwoort (5); Cornelis de Hooghe (1); Johannes Rutlinger (1). The English names are: Augustine Ryther (4); Francis Scatter (2); Nicholas Reynolds (1).[17] Augustine Ryther (fl 1576–1595) was to become a leading instrument-maker. This migration of skilled engravers occurred throughout the sixteenth century, but particularly during the middle years when the grip of Spanish religious persecution was tightening on the Netherlands, finally to result in the Revolt which broke out in 1564.

The main materials used for making mathematical instruments were brass and wood, usually box wood. Prior to the sixteenth century, brass needed for such uses as memorials had been imported from the Continent, and thus was expensive. Now, with growing demand – for brass enabled instruments to be made with more accurate scales – the Royal Charters for the Company of Mineral and Battery Works and the Company of Mines Royal for the production, *inter alia*, of brass and brass plate, were granted in May 1568, allowing English manufacture for the first time.[18] Humphrey Cole, of whom more will be said later, was closely involved in the setting up of the Mineral and Battery Works, which necessitated bringing in German craftsmen to train Englishmen in metal-working skills, and in prospecting for ores.[19] Cole was engraver of dies for the Royal Mint, as well as the leading instrument-maker of the period.

The instruments

The instruments being made in London at this period were those described as mathematical instruments, a term which includes sundials, navigational and survey-ing instruments, as well as certain drawing and calculating instruments. There were spectacle-makers from 1300, but not until the seventeenth century were there optical instruments – also a Dutch invention – and not until the end of that century did the trade in philosophical instruments arise. During the eighteenth century all three groups were particularly active in London, then the world's leading centre.[20]

London kept its virtual monopoly of the scientific instrument-making trade until the nineteenth century, when subsidiary provincial centres became established. Little is known about the origins of the trade, but some recent work is beginning to reveal a broad outline of the probable development. Some extant instruments also present vital evidence, and some of these have only recently been acquired by museums.

Astronomical instruments, the astrolabe, equatorium, and large angular measuring instruments for observatory use, have received a good share of scholarly attention;[21] surveying instruments rather less.[22] But there is little material so far on the structure of the trade for all types of instrument, so any comments must be somewhat tentative.

Studies have been made during this century of a few European makers of the post-medieval period; these include:

Jean Fusoris (c1365–1436)
Peter Apian of Ingolstadt (1495–1552)
Thomas Gemini of London (fl 1524–62)
Humphrey Cole of London (?1530–91)
Christoph Schissler the Elder of Augsburg (fl 1546–1605)
Egnazio Danti of Florence (fl 1570)
Joost Bürgi of Kassel (1552–1632)[23]

In the period we have to consider, the great influence on instrument design was Gemma Frisius, and his co-operation with Gerard Mercator. Then there are the three relatives of Gemma, Gualterus Arsenius, and Regnerus and Ferdinandus Arsenius, the products of whose workshops were disseminated in Europe through the agency of the Plantin printing house in Antwerp.[24] Here may be found the source of influence on Thomas Gemini in London, and it may be remarked that an astrolabe made by him in 1559 came into the possession of John Greaves (1602–52), Gresham Professor, and later Savilian Professor of Astronomy at Oxford from 1643 to 1648.[25] This astrolabe was taken by Greaves on his journey to the Levant, and was used with other instruments to determine the latitude of Rhodes. In 1659 it was presented, together with some instruments by Elias Allen, to the University of Oxford, where they remain to-day. The astrolabe is engraved with the Royal Arms and cipher, ER, and Elizabeth's name and titles. Its date is of more than passing significance. Elizabeth came to the throne on 17 November 1558; scientific instrument-making in London owes a debt to the long, threatened, and yet settled reign of that Queen.

By 1600, the number of men trained as engravers had increased, and workshops had grown in number and size. Instruments became more complex and varied, with competition in producing new designs to catch attention and to do down a rival. Earlier, the craftsman had worked in collaboration with the scholar-inventor; now he was to become capable of independent invention. Wealthy men became more interested in scientific matters, and elaborately embellished instruments were provided for their delectation. Naturally it is such pieces that tend to be preserved rather than the work-a-day instruments, with the result that our museum collections are weighted towards the former. It has been asked, where are the instruments used by the man in field? Was there really any surveying done? Was the forestaff really used on board ship? This is because only three Elizabethan theodolites, only one or two forestaves, and no plane table, remain from this period. On the other hand, there are as many as 145 of Habermel's gilded masterpieces, made for Rudolph II in about 1600, extant in collections.[26] This is why some have thought that these designs were just cabinet pieces, while others think them nineteenth-century imitations.

As Joyce Brown has rightly pointed out, an important factor in the establishment of the instrument-making trade was the way in which it could become grafted on to the existing guild structure.[27] The City of London Guilds were medieval and, by the sixteenth century, what are known as the Twelve Great Livery Companies had emerged as leaders. To learn a craft and to practise it meant that an apprenticeship had to be served, and the arrangement properly recorded and approved by a City Company. Practising a new craft, instrument-makers had to find a company as best they might; one way was to join a father's company, whichever it might be, under the patrimony arrangement. New companies were formed, of course: the Spectacle-Makers in 1629, the Clockmakers in 1631. But the mathematical instrument-makers were captured to a great and surprising extent by one of the Twelve Great Livery Companies, the Grocers. Once a master-apprentice succession was established, the instrument-makers remained in the Company, and so a school was built up. This is what happened, and the succession has been graphically recorded and explained by Joyce Brown in her book published in 1979.[28] Her Table II of the craft tree shows the later development of the trade in the Grocers' Company through two centuries.

One of the founders of the London trade was Thomas Gemini, alias Lambrit (c1510–1562), who came from a village near Liège.[29] Being a member of the Dutch Church in Austin Friars, he was presumably a Protestant refugee. He was an engraver, who made his reputation with his plates for his own printing of the *Anatomy* of Vesalius (1545), earning himself an annuity of £10 from Henry VIII. At Blackfriars, he carried on the business of map-engraver and mathematical instrument-maker. An astrolabe made by him is in a Belgian museum, bearing the arms of the Duke of Northumber-

40. This map ascribable to Matthew Nelson and drawn for Corpus Christi College, somewhat before 1605, illustrates his somewhat austere manner.

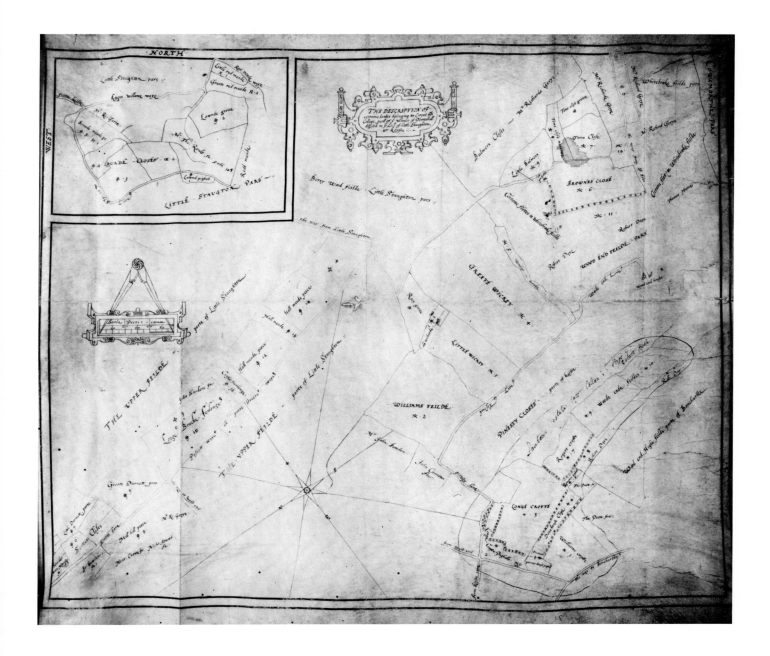

41. and **42.** Vernacular architecture in early seventeenth century Kesteven is illustrated by these two extracts (Barkston and Beckingham) from Langdon's volume of surveys made for Corpus Christi College in 1609.

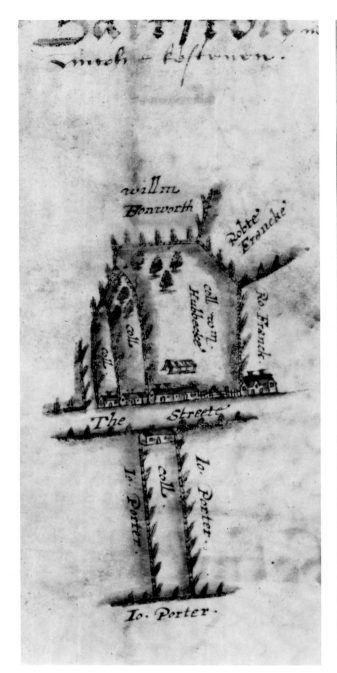

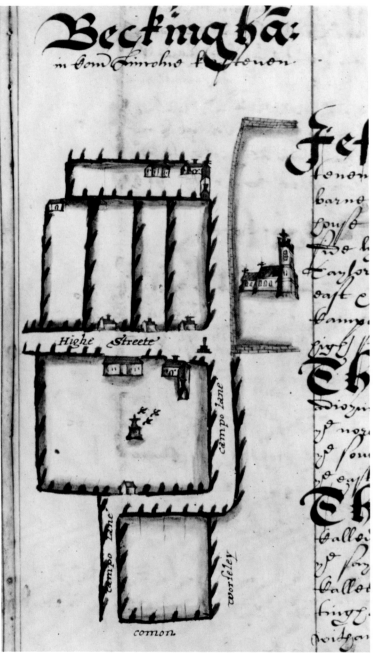

43. Cartouche and title from a map of Eynsham South Field drawn by Henry Wilcocke in 1615, in the manner of Thomas Langdon.

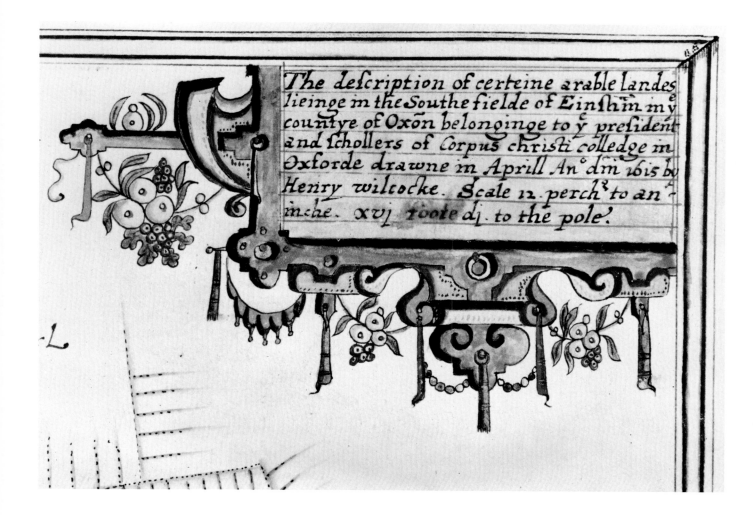

The description of certeine arable landes lieinge in the Southe fielde of Einſhīm in y̅ countye of Oxōn belonginge to y̅ preſident and ſchollers of Corpus christi colledge in Oxforde drawne in Aprill An° dm 1615 by Henry wilcocke. Scale 12. perchᵗ to an inche. xvj roote dj. to the pole.

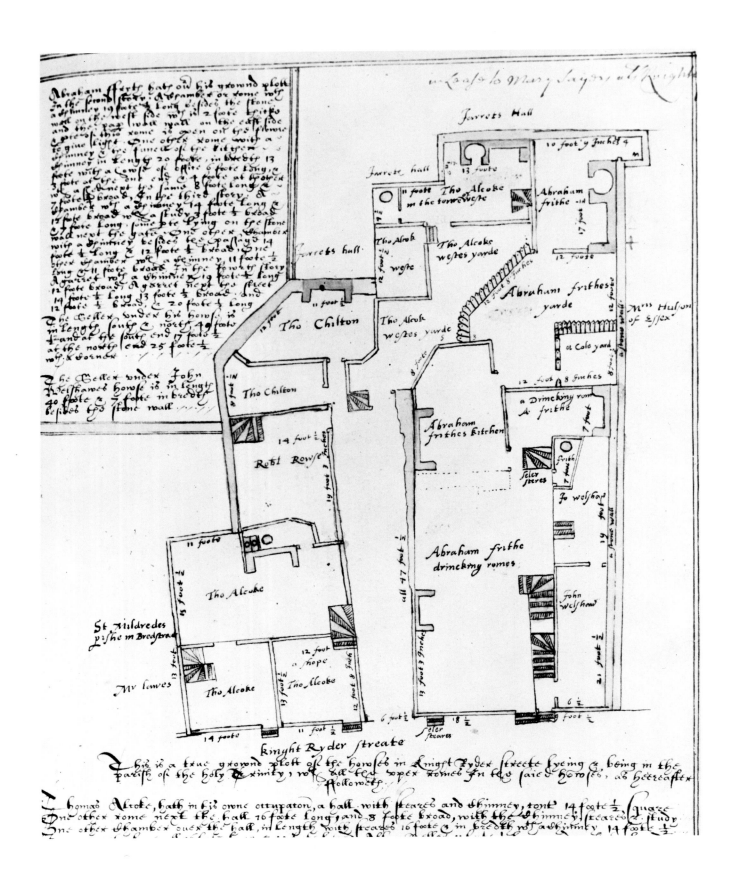

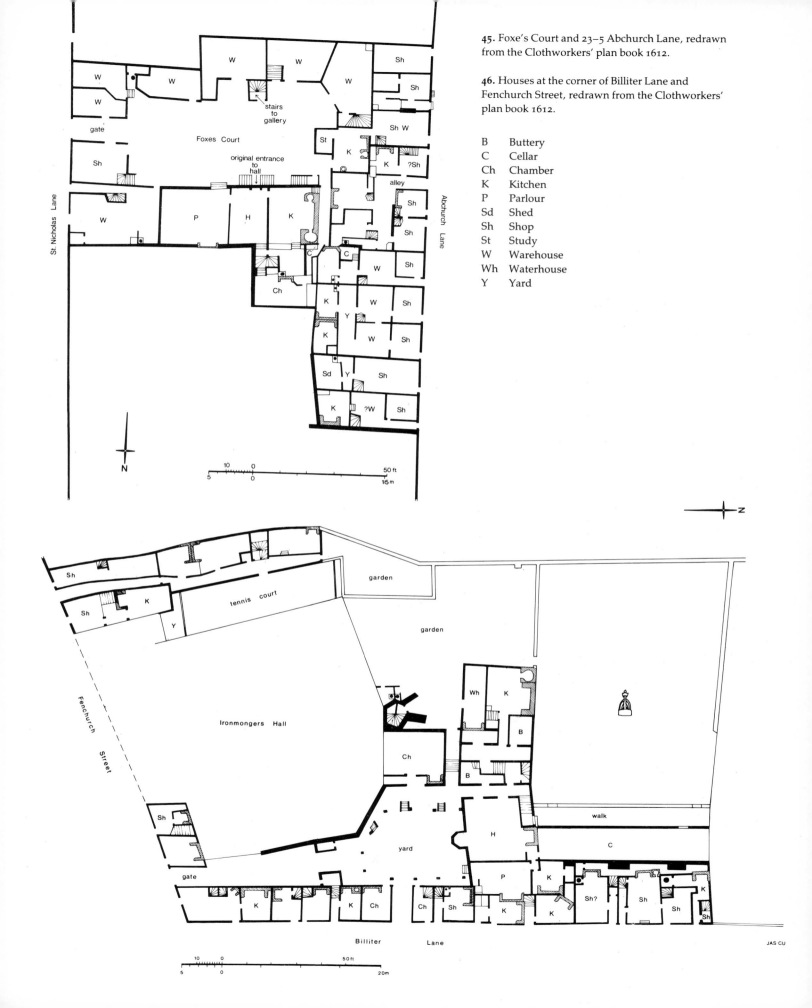

45. Foxe's Court and 23–5 Abchurch Lane, redrawn from the Clothworkers' plan book 1612.

46. Houses at the corner of Billiter Lane and Fenchurch Street, redrawn from the Clothworkers' plan book 1612.

B   Buttery
C   Cellar
Ch   Chamber
K   Kitchen
P   Parlour
Sd   Shed
Sh   Shop
St   Study
W   Warehouse
Wh   Waterhouse
Y   Yard

Foxes Court

stairs to gallery

gate

St. Nicholas Lane

original entrance to hall

Abchurch Lane

alley

N

10 0 50 ft
5 0 15 m

garden

garden

tennis court

Ironmongers Hall

Fenchurch Street

Billiter Lane

gate

yard

walk

10 0 50 ft
5 0 20 m

JAS CU

48. Theodolite signed and dated H. Côle, 1586.
(Description p. 102)

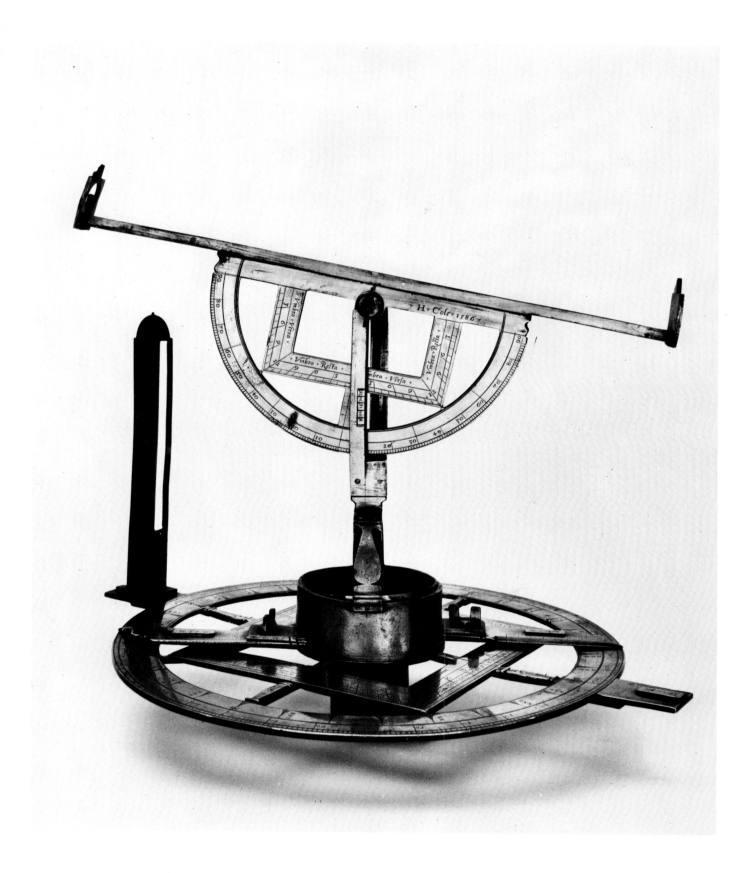

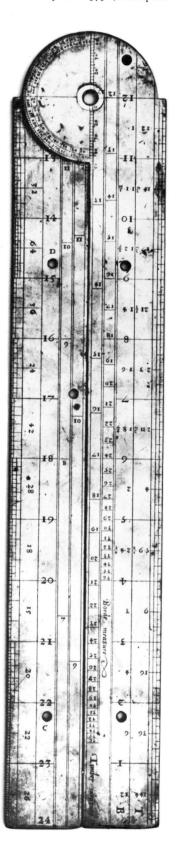

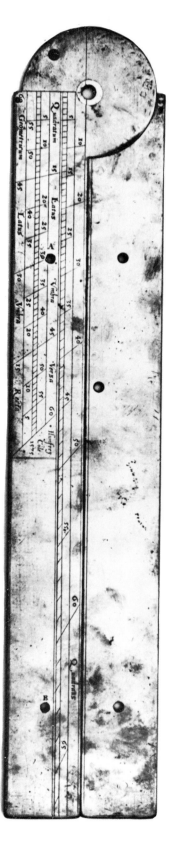

50. Plane table alidade signed and dated H. Côle, 1582. (Description p. 102)

51. Surveyor's folding rule signed and dated Humfrey Côle 1575. (Description p. 103)

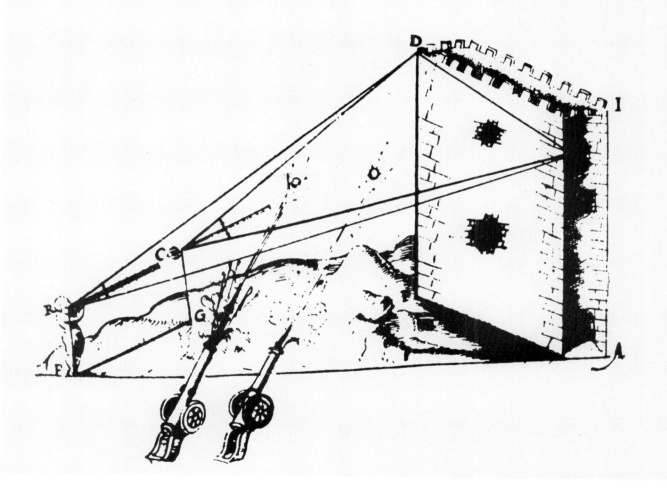

Saber a distancia de olho à cousa vista q̃ chamão linha
visual. E na artelharia se cobrara a hũa fortaleza ou naao
e juntamẽte o q̃ estam apartadas duas cousas hũa da outra
E o q̃ tem de largo hum edeficio pelles instrumẽ atras exẽpli
ficados...

LIBRI .VI. TRACT. SECVNDVS

ut feʒ extrēitates baculi pui impofiti furfū & deorfū tē‧
dant‧quo facto:accedas aut recedas/ donec p has ext rēi
tates rei cōfpiciende/ fupiorē & inferiorē terminos vi‧
deas‧& fgna locū ſtationis tuæ‧ Dehinc baculū puū m
de foramine priore extrahas & in proximū retro (fi ac
cedere volueris) aut ante (fi retrocedere intendas) po‧
ne‧& iterʒ accededo & retrocededo p extremitates bacu
li parui/terminos rei vifę cōfpicias:locūcʒ ſtationis illi
us fignes‧ ꝗntū em eſt
int ifta‧& priorē ſtato
nē tāta eſt altitudo rei
vifæ‧ Sic fi fi mō lati‧
tudinem inueſtigabi s
fi baculū ita vertas ut
extrēitates baculi pui
dextrorfū & finiſtror
fum ꝑtendant‧ Sūt &
pla alia in‧
genia & iſt/
rumēta p ꝗ
ea ꝗ dicta fe
iueſtigant‧
deꝗbus bre
uitatis itm̄
caufa fuper
fedendū eſt
ſtilū ad alia
vertamus‧

I iiij

BACVLVS IACOB

55. Leonard Digges's 'the profitable staffe' from L. Digges *Tectonicon* (1592).

The vſe of the profitable ſtaffe. 23

The making of this profitable
Rodde or Staffe.

The firſt Chapter.

YE ſhall prepare two ſmall, ſtreight, ſtiffe, roũd, oʒ rather ſquare rods, of metal oʒ of wood, well plained, of like bigneſſe and length. Although it make no matter of what length, yet to auoyd the erroʒs, which little Inſtruments & ſhoʒt ſtaues bʒing, and alſo to beare with the rude bnwoonted handling of ſuch Artificers: let your Rods be each fiue, oʒ oʒ the leaſt thʒée foote, and euery foote diuided in 12. euen parts oʒ Inches, as ye ſée a. b. & c.d. Theſe rods muſt be foʒged with a vice in the end of thʒ to ioine readily 10.oʒ 6. Foot in length, (when time requireth) as the figure e. f. ſheweth. Alſo ye muſt get (by the helpe of ſome Craftſman) 4. other like rods, the longer g. 2.foot: the next h. 1. foote: the other i. 6. Inches, then k. 3. Inches, the laſt and ſhoʒteſt l. 1. Inch, and ½. Each of theſe muſt haue in their midſt a hole, that the long ſtaffe of 10. foote may be put thʒough them, and they mooued on him at pleaſure

up and downe, alwayes cutting the longer ſtaffe e.f. Squirewiſe, and made to tarie on any diuiſion, as occaſion ſhall be giuen

THE
DESCRIPTION
and vſe of the
SECTOR.
The Croſſe-ſtaffe and
other inſtruments.
For ſuch as are ſtudious
of Mathematicall
practiſe.
AT LONDON
Printed by Williã Jones.
and are to be ſold by
Edmund Weauer.
1624.

57. A hexagon lattice of 12 to 14 miles to cover an assumed isotropic Devon.

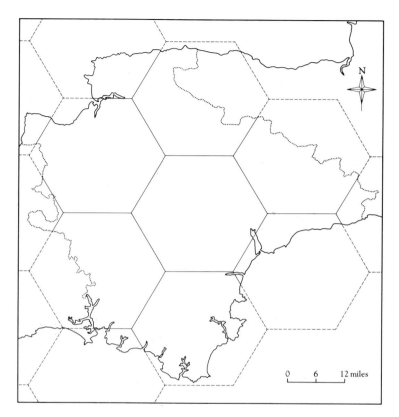

58. A hexagon lattice of 6 miles to cover an isotropic Devon landscape.

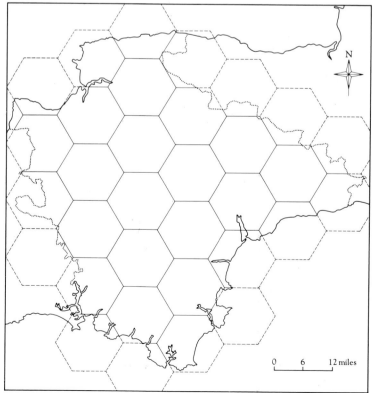

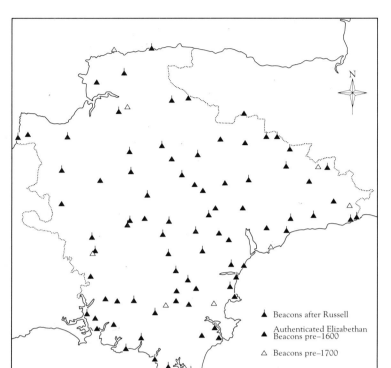

59. The beacons of Devon.

Beacons after Russell

Authenticated Elizabethan
Beacons pre–1600

△ Beacons pre–1700

0   6   12 miles

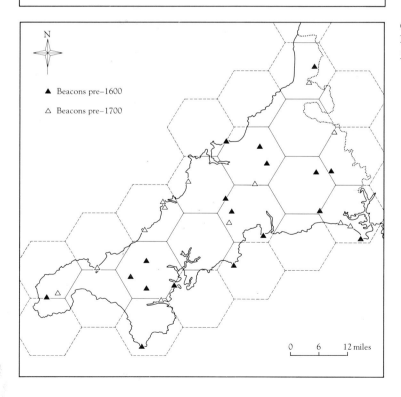

60. The beacons of Cornwall. A 6-mile hexagon lattice is superimposed for comparison with plate 58.

▲ Beacons pre–1600

△ Beacons pre–1700

0   6   12 miles

land and of Edward VI.[30] It was made in 1552, possibly for the expedition to find the North-East Passage. In 1555 Gemini printed the *Prognostications* of Leonard Digges (*c*1520–*c*1559), and the following year, Digges' *A Boke Named Tectonicon*, which was the first general work in English on practical surveying.[31] It was written for 'Surveyors, Landmeaters, Ioyners, Carpenters, and Masons', and attempted to remedy the ordinary surveyor's ignorance of mathematics. It described some instruments to help him, which could either be made by himself, or obtained from Thomas Gemini; these included the 'carpenter's ruler' and 'carpenter's squire', both of which incorporated sights and a plumb-bob, and a version of the cross staff.[32]

The theodolite appears in Leonard Digges' posthumously published book, *A Geometrical Practice Named Pantometria* (1571). R.T. Gunther, the first Curator of the Museum at Oxford, was of the opinion that: 'the first invention of this important instrument in its simplest form is due to Leonard Digges', an event supposed to have occurred in about 1550.[33] However, it is more likely that Digges introduced into England the invention of the German, Waldseemüller, whose theodolite (which he called a Polymetrum) was illustrated in 1512,[34] and that his other influences were Apian and Gemma Frisius. The Digges instrument consisted of a horizontal circle divided into 360 degrees, with a semi-circle at right-angles above it that could measure angles of elevation. Both circles contained within them a geometrical square. An astrolabe could be used for horizontal or vertical angles, and one can see that the theodolite, combining together the means to make both measurements, can be said to derive from the astrolabe.

The art of circle-dividing was the truly critical part of mathematical instrument-making, one that needed the greatest skill; therefore, a fine astrolabist could be expected to make the theodolite and other angle-measuring instruments. Three Elizabethan theodolites of the Digges type are in existence, though one is partly restored. They are a Humphrey Cole, dated 1574; another by him dated 1586; and one by Augustine Ryther, dated 1590 (pl. 47, 48, 49).

Some names of London instrument-makers have been mentioned already, their existence known because a few of their products have come down to us. But there is another way in which it is possible to find out about men working in this trade – that is, through contemporary accounts by scholars or professional men who employed them. The inability of the surveyor in the field properly to understand what he was doing led Edward Worsop to publish, in 1582, his corrective, which carried his advertisement for several London instrument-makers because 'many that would provide [*ie* obtain] such things, knowe not where to have them'.[35] The makers' names he gives are: for metal instruments, Humphrey Cole (North Door, St Paul's), John Bull (Exchange Gate); for wooden instruments, John Reade (Hosier Lane), James Lockerson (Dowgate), John Reynolds (Tower Hill).

A work published by an Oxford graduate, Cyprian Lucar, in 1590, gave an account of surveying practice, using the plane table.[36] This was the first description in English of the device, which is rectangular, with an outer frame to hold the paper down, and a rule or alidade. He itemized the surveyor's kit of instruments, and listed makers who could supply them, as follows: 'geometrical tables with their feete, frames, rulers, compasses [dividers], and squires [squares] are made and sold by Iohn Reynolds, dwelling right against the southeast end of Barking churchyard in tower streete within London, and by Iohn Reade, and Christopher Paine, dwelling in Hosier lane

... wyer lines ... may be bought in crooked lane neare vnto Eastcheape in London, ...'

The man who must be regarded as London's foremost mathematical instrument-maker of the sixteenth century is Humphrey Cole (?1530–91).[37] Over fifty years ago Dr Gunther published a paper on the various products of Cole, so a brief summary is all that is needed here.[38] Cole was from the north of England, and was employed as an engraver and Sinker of the Stamps at the Mint. He engraved for the printer Jugge, and he undertook to supply all the instruments described in the 1571 edition of Digges' *Pantometria*. Cole's masterpiece must surely be the large, two-foot diameter astrolabe, dated 1575, in the possession of the University of St Andrews.[39] This has several resemblances to the Gemini astrolabe made for Elizabeth I, both instruments having on the back a horizontal projection of the sphere derived from the planisphere of Gemma Frisius. Many instruments signed and dated by Cole survive, and they include: a ring dial; the so-called Drake's dial of 1569, which is a compendium of instruments; other compendia; a horizontal sundial; an armillary sphere; a nocturnal; the gunner's combination compass in the British Museum; a small astrolabe given to Henry, Prince of Wales; and an alidade for a plane table, recently purchased by the Museum of the History of Science in Oxford.[40] Cole's production is both varied and extensive, judging by the twenty-two extant instruments. It is clear that he had an influence on subsequent makers, as would be expected. This is shown by the Ryther theodolite, and the pocket dials by Charles Whitwell and Elias Allen. Although he was free of the Goldsmiths' Company and not the Grocers' Company, Cole may be said to be the originator of that line of craftsmen.[41]

Another recent acquisition at Oxford is a sector by Robert Beckit dated 1597 (pl. 52). This resembles the one described by Thomas Hood (fl 1582–98) who, following a Privy Council recommendation that citizens should be instructed in military matters, was appointed mathematical lecturer in London. Hood published in 1598 a text entitled: *The Making and Vse of the Geometrical Instrument called a Sector*.[42] The Museum has another sector of the Hood type, which is undated. These pre-date the publication of Galileo's sector (1606).[43] As for Robert Beckit himself, very little is known except that he engraved five maps for the London edition of 1598 of Jan Huygen van Linschoten's *Discours of Voyages into ye Easte & West Indies* . . .[44] These two recent finds add greatly to the realization that, by 1600, London was a centre of more than parochial importance for the mathematical instrument-making trade.

By comparing extant instruments, the influence of Cole on Augustine Ryther (theodolite) and on Charles Whitwell (astronomical compendium) can readily be seen. If an examination of the James Kynvyn instruments in Florence were to be made they, too, would probably show Cole's influence.[45] Certainly by 1600 a tradition had been well started in the style in which mathematical instruments were made in London, that distinguishes them from contemporary instruments made on the Continent.

The poet, Gabriel Harvey, in a note on his copy of John Blagrave, *The Mathematical Jewel* (1585), made a connexion of his own: James Kynvyn 'of London, neere Powles. A fine workman & mie kinde frend: first commended vnto me bie M. Digges & M. Blagrave himself . . . He & old Humfrie Cole, mie mathematical mechanicians . . .'[46] Kynvyn flourished between 1570 and 1610, and his workshop was, like Cole's, near St. Paul's. One of his products, a pocket dial bearing the arms of the Earl of Essex and the date 1593, is in the British Museum, and four others are in the Science Museum in Florence.[47]

Little is known about Augustine Ryther (fl 1576–95), but the recent work of Joyce Brown has ably pointed up his position at the top of the craft tree in the Grocers' Company. He was an engraver of distinction, and signed some of his maps 'Augustinus Ryther Anglus', to distinguish himself from the Flemish engravers. It has been suggested that he was born in Leeds.[48] Cole, too, stressed his English birth, on a map of the Holy Land published in Jugge's edition of the Bible of 1572: 'graven bi Hvmfray Cole Goldsmith a English man born in y north and pertayning to ye Mint in the Tower. 1572'.[49] The earliest signed work of Ryther is a couple of maps dated 1576, engraved for Christopher Saxton. Only one instrument is known, a theodolite in Florence, signed: *ARyther fecit* 1590.[50] This is very similar in construction to that of Cole, dated 1586, at Oxford, there being minor differences in the upper sights and in the size of the compass box. The Ryther instrument appears so exactly like the theodolite depicted in Blaeu's *Atlas* of 1664, that it is hard to believe it was not a model for that work.[51]

For nine years from 17 December 1582, Ryther took as his apprentice Charles Whitwell (fl 1590-1611), who obtained his Freedom of the Grocers' Company on 10 November 1590.[52] Hood advertised on the title-page of his book on the *Sector* (1598) that 'the instrument is made by Charles Whitwell, dwelling without Temple Barre against St Clements Church'. Maps and instruments bearing his name exist, there being at least ten instruments in museums. There are eight men among his known apprentices, the most famous being the incomparable Elias Allen (c1588–1653), who became Free of the Grocers' Company on 7 July 1612, having served about nine years.[53]

Appendix 1

Humphrey Cole's extant instruments

The present tally of Cole's instruments is twenty-two signed by Cole, eighteen of which are dated; two signed 'V.C.', one dated, the other not; one unsigned and undated, but attributed to Cole. These are listed below, and the author would be *most appreciative* if any reader can give further locations. (An asterisk * indicates a surveying instrument.)

NO	DATE	TYPE	SIGNATURE	LOCATION	INVENTORY
1.	1568	Compendium	Hvmfray Coole	Oxford	LE.1
2.	1569	Compendium	Humfray Colle	Greenwich	D.318
3.	c1570*	Gunner's compasses	Humfray Coolle	BM	78 11–1, 114
4.	c1570*	Quadrant-dial	Humfray Colle	Oxford	50–21
5.	1574*	Theodolite	H. Côle	Greenwich	SI/T.1
6.	1574	Astrolabe	Humfrey Cole	BM	55 12–1, 223
7.	1574*	Surveyor's folding rule	Humfrey Côle	Private Colln	
8.	1575	Surveyor's folding rule	Humfrey Côle	Oxford	50–41
9.	1575*	Gunner's compasses	H. Cole	BM	1912 11–1, 1
10.	1575	Compendium	Humfrey Cole	BM	88 12–1, 293
11.	1575	Ring dial	H. Côle	BM	1905 6–8, 1
12.	1575	Compass dial	Humfrey Cole	Edinburgh	
13.	1575*	Surveyor's folding rule	Humfrey Côle	Florence	2527
14.	1575	Astrolabe	Humfridus Côle	St Andrews	
15.	c1575	Nocturnal	H. Cole	BM	57 11–16, 2
16.	1579	Horizontal dial	H. Cole	Oxford	LE.232
17.	1579	Compendium	Humfrey Côle	Liège	505
18.	1582*	Plane table alidade	H. Côle	Oxford	80–22
19.	1582	Horizontal dial	Humfrae Colle	Greenwich	D.249
20.	1582	Armillary Sphere	Humphrey Cole	St Andrews	
21.	1586*	Theodolite	H. Cole	Oxford	24–37
22.	1590	Compendium	Humfrey Cole	Horniman	31.183 A
	c1554	Compendium	V.C.	Oxford	52–74
	1557	Compendium	V.C.	Chicago	M363
	c1575	Gunner's folding rule	Unsigned	Woolwich	XXIV.200

Locations

BM	British Museum	Horniman	Horniman Museum, London
Chicago	Adler Planetarium	Liège	Musée de la Vie Wallonne
Edinburgh	National Museum of Antiquities	Oxford	Museum of the History of Science
Florence	Museo di Storia della Scienza	St Andrews	University of St Andrews
Greenwich	National Maritime Museum	Woolwich	Museum of Artillery

The two compendia signed 'V.C.' were made eleven and fourteen years before the main group of extant instruments signed and dated by Cole. They have been attributed to Cole on the assumption that the letters stand for Vmfrey Cole. Cole has nowhere else used this spelling for his first name. The character of the letter and numeral forms is not that of the signed Cole instruments. Both the V.C. compendia have names of some English towns in the Latin form, whereas the two earliest (1568, 1569) Cole instruments, also compendia, use no Latin forms. The latitudes for towns given on these two Cole compendia are accurate, *eg* London 51° 34'. The earlier V.C. gives latitudes many of which are a degree too high, *eg* London 52° 30'. The later V.C. gives co-latitudes, *eg* London 38° 0'. The earlier, *c*1554, has plates of tables very closely resembling those engraved for Digges, *Prognostications*, published in 1555 by Thomas Gemini. It is therefore unlikely that these two instruments were the work of Humphrey Cole, and they were probably the work of a Flemish craftsman employed by Thomas Gemini.[54]

The unsigned rule is described by the Museum of Artillery as a 'Gunner's brass folding rule, *circa* 1590'. Dr Mary Holbrook, in the course of preparing the British National Inventory of Scientific Instruments (projected publication date 1983), described this instrument as a 'Gunner's folding rule, sector shaped . . . brass, closed length 6½ in. Scales relate to gunnery . . . Unsigned, but similar to instruments by Humphrey Cole, *c*1575'.

Appendix 2

Descriptions of the instruments illustrated plates 47–52

Plate 47. Theodolite 1574

Signed and dated: + H + Côle + 1574 +

Brass; diameter of azimuth circle 172mm. The altitude semi-circle is a reconstruction; the compass box is probably original. Unlike the later theodolite, the azimuth circle is made of a solid piece of brass, with the 'Geometricall + Square' and the degree scale engraved on it. The edge is divided 0°–360° by half degree intervals, with, in addition, the indications for 0°–90°–0°–90°–0°. Inside the geometrical square are engraved the 32 points of the compass, each point divided into eighths (256 divisions in the circle). The compass is complete, and the declination is marked on the base of the box by a line about 12° East of North. This is consistent with the date engraved on the instrument. Engraved on the underside of the circle is the name: + Edward + Williams +.

National Maritime Museum, Greenwich. SI/T.1

Plate 48. Theodolite 1586

Signed and dated Y H Y Cole Y 1586 Y

Brass; diameter of azimuth circle 190mm; diameter of altitude semi-circle 115mm. The azimuth circle is divided from 0°–360° by one degree intervals, and within this scale are marked the 32 points of the compass. Inside the circle is a geometrical square. The altitude semi-circle is divided in single degrees from 90°–0°–90°, and inside is a shadow square. Above the compass box hangs a levelling plummet. Provision is made for four sights, two fixed at the North and South points, and two on the azimuth rule; the dovetails are numbered to correspond to the removable sights, only one of which remains. The compass-needle and glass are also missing. Two wing nuts attach the compass box and vertical circle assembly to the rule, so that the azimuth circle can be used by itself, and so that the vertical circle can be fitted to a plane table alidade. This is the earliest complete theodolite known.

Museum of the History of Science, Oxford. 24–37

Plate 49. Theodolite 1590

Signed and dated: ★ *ARyther + fecit* + 1590 ★ Brass; diameter of azimuth circle 200mm; diameter of altitude semi-circle 100mm.

Both the azimuth circle and the altitude semi-circle are divided to one degree, the former being marked 0°–360° and the latter 90°–0°–90°. Inside the semi-circle is a shadow square, and inside the azimuth circle is a geometrical square. The pillar above the compass case has provision for a levelling plummet, now missing. It is striking how closely this theodolite resembles that signed by Cole, the only material difference lying in the absence of fixed sights at the North and South points.

Museo di Storia Della Scienze, Florence. 240

Plate 50. Plane table alidade 1582

Signed and dated: H· Cole· 1582.

Brass; overall length 445mm; width 25mm. The sides are bevelled, with the exception of one end which is scolloped. The English inch is marked out from the top of the bevel at one end, extending to 17 inches divided into 1/8ths. There is a further run of 17 inches each divided into a different number of parts denoted by engraved numbers, which are: 7, 20, 21, 22, 24, 26, 27, 28, 30, 32, 36, 40, 48, 64, 56, 18. This gives a choice of scales for use on maps.

The two holes near the middle are threaded, and were for fixing a sight for use with a plane table. Cole claimed that he could supply the instruments referred to in Leonard Digges, *A Geometrical Practice Named Pantometria* (London, 1571), where the theodolite was described. His son, Thomas Digges, added to the 1591 edition an appendix at the end of the First Book called *Longimetra*: 'A note touching a Platting Instrument for such as are ignorant of Arithmeticall Calculations. Some take the Semi-circle of my Topological Instrument [theodolite], setting the Perpendiculare thereof vpon a straighte long Ruler deuided into a thousande or more equall parts, and insteade of the Horizontall Circle vse only a plaine Table or boarde: whereon a large Sheet of Parchement or Paper may be fastened. . . . This being an Instrument onely for the ignorante and vnlearned, that haue no knowledge of Noumbers, and not to be practized but in fayre weather, and where yee may haue time sufficient euen in the Fielde to pricke and set downe the Charte.'

The curious divisions of an inch require an explanation. Plane tables are not particularly large, and can measure 15 × 12 inches, which can take a full sheet of foolscap paper measuring 17 × 13½ inches. A surveyor would wish his plan to fill the sheet of paper, accordingly he would need to choose a convenient scale. For example:

110 yards   in 15 inches could use a scale of 1:7
300 yards   in 15 inches could use a scale of 1:20
400 perches in 15 inches could use a scale of 1:27
440 yards   in 15 inches could use a scale of 1:30
600 yards   in 15 inches could use a scale of 1:40
960 feet   in 15 inches could use a scale of 1:64

This is a possible explanation for the series of divisions of the inch engraved on this alidade, and a comparison can be made with a surveyor's folding rule which has twelve choices (pl. 51), and a gunner's compasses with a choice of twenty-four (BM 1912 11–1, 1).

Museum of the History of Science, Oxford. 80–22

Plate 51. Surveyor's folding rule 1575

Signed and dated: ★ *Humfrey · Côle · 1575* ★
Brass; radius 305mm (12 inch).
On one side are: scales of *Timber-measure* and *Borde-measure* for estimating volume and area; an inch scale numbered from 1 to 24; the inches divided on one limb into 1/8ths and on the other limb into the following parts: 8, 32, 64, 36, 24, 42, 28, 18, 15, 20, 22, 26. At the joint is a degree scale divided to 2° intervals and marked 0°–90° and 90°–0°. The inside edge of each limb is divided 500 to 0 (at centre of joint) to 500 in 2 unit divisions, so making 1,000 parts in 24 inches. The joint may be locked at the 90° or 180° positions.

The other side is provided with a quadrant to 66°, and a shadow square, both scales for use with the joint locked at right angles.

The rule is pierced with four holes marked A,B,C,D, for fixing sights; the hole at the joint can fix the rule to a tripod. When locked at 180°, this rule was capable of being used as a plane table alidade with the inner edge in 1,000 parts as mentioned by Digges (see the alidade above, plate 50).

Museum of the History of Science, Oxford. 50–41.

Plate 52. Surveyor's sector 1597

Signed and dated: ★ *Robertus* ★ *Beckit* ★ *fecit* ★ *1597* ★
Brass, with iron points; radius, including points, 329 mm.
The brass limbs are engraved on one side with *Power of Lynes*, and *Coards of a circle*; while on the other side is a line of numbers (0 to 112) for calculations made with a pair of dividers. One limb slides over a wide, curved arc of brass. The two sequences under 'Power of Lynes' bear the following numbers that represent ratios:
1(at ends) ½, ⅓, ¼, ⅕, ⅙, ⅐, ⅛, ⅑, ¹⁄₁₀
With the limbs open, the line between the pair of points 1:3 (for example) will, when squared, give an area a third of the square of the line between the points of the limbs. The two sequences under 'Coards of a circle' bear the numbers 3 to 12. These give the lengths of the chords of a circle, relative to a diameter equal to the opening at the points, subtending such a portion of the whole circumference as is signified by the numbers. For example, the distance between the 5s will give the chords for an inscribed pentagon.

On the brass arc are points numbered 3, 4, and 5, which give the angles for 3, 4, and 5 sided figures ie, 60°, 90°, 108°. On the same side of the arc are three engraved scales with their ends in common, calibrated from 0–180, 0–144, 0–104, and subdivided to ½ units in each case. These represent 18 inches divided into tenths, eighths, and sixths, the measure being taken from the tip of the iron points at the ends of the limbs.

On the other side of the instrument is the line of numbers, which is used with a pair of dividers for calculations based on the principle of similar triangles. The brass arc is engraved with one scale of degrees, 0°–110°, numbered in 10s, and divided to ¼°.

Holes in the limbs at the ends are for sights, and at the centre for fixing to a post and for a sight.

The sector was invented earlier than the slide-rule, and persisted in use until the middle of the nineteenth century. The popularity of the sector owed much to Galileo, who published a description of his *compasso geometrico e militare* in 1606. However, there were sixteenth-century precursors of the Galilean instrument, one of which was the sector described by Thomas Hood (*fl* 1582–1598) who, following a Privy Council recommendation that citizens should be instructed in military matters, was appointed to a mathematical lecturership in London. The sector resembles that described by Hood, as may be seen from an illustration in Hood's book *The Making and Vse of the Geometricall Instrument, called a Sector. . .*, London

[?1598], and it is dated the year before the probable date of that publication.

The Museum also possesses a smaller and undated sector of the Hood-type, which differs in several respects from this one, which probably represents an earlier stage in the development of the instrument. Little is known of the maker of this instrument, Robert Beckit, except that he engraved some five maps for the London edition, 1598, of Jan Huygen van Linschoten's *Discours of Voyages into ye Easte & West Indies.* . . .
Museum of the History of Science, Oxford. 80–8

1. This book was reprinted in Amsterdam, 1974, under the name John Fitzherbert. The *Dictionary of National Biography* makes Anthony Fitzherbert, the younger brother, the author. The matter is discussed in A.W. Richeson, *English Land Measuring to 1800: Instruments and Practice* (Cambridge, Mass, 1966), pp. 31–33, showing that John is more likely. In support, two works are cited: R.F.C. Fitzherbert, 'The Authorship of the "Book of Husbandry" and the "Book of Surveying"', *English Historical Review*, 12 (1897), 225–36; E.F. Gay, 'The Authorship of the Book of Husbandry and the Book of Surveying', *Quarterly Journal of Economics*, 18 (1904), 588–90.

2. Richeson, *Land Measuring*, p. 35.

3. J.M. Pullan, *The History of the Abacus* (London, 1969), p. 43.

4. Pullan, *Abacus*, chapter 4, 'Counter-Casting to Pen-Reckoning', pp. 43–56; Francis P. Barnard, *The Casting-Counter and the Counting-Board. A Chapter in the History of Numismatics and Early Arithmetic* (Oxford, 1917; reprinted Castle Cary, Somerset, 1981), especially pp. 230–320.

5. A.W. Richeson, 'The First Arithmetic Printed in English', *Isis*, 37 (1947), 47–56.

6. The first edition is often dated 1542, but see Joy B. Easton, 'The Early Editions of Robert Recorde's *Ground of Artes*', *Isis*, 58 (1967), 515–32; see also her article on Recorde in *Dictionary of Scientific Biography* [hereafter cited as *DSB*], edited by C.C. Gillispie, xɪ (1975), 338–40. For the practice, see Barnard, *Casting-Counter*, pp. 256–66.

7. E.G.R. Taylor, *The Mathematical Practitioners of Tudor & Stuart England* (Cambridge, 1954), p. 313.

8. Easton, *DSB*, p. 339.

9. Taylor, *Mathematical Practitioners*, p. 313.

10. Peter J. French, *John Dee. The World of an Elizabethan Magus* (London, 1972), pp. 4–5, 28–9.

11. French, *Dee*, p. 166; Joy B. Easton, 'Dee, John', *DSB*, ɪᴠ (1971), 5–6; Taylor, *Mathematical Practitioners*, pp. 34, 320.

12. French, *Dee*, p. 167.

13. John J. Roche, 'The Radius Astronomicus in England', *Annals of Science*, 38 (1981), 1–32 (p. 16).

14. Roche, *Radius Astronomicus*, p. 18. See also below pp. 107–9.

15. Roche, *Radius Astronomicus*, p. 19.

16. F.A.B. Ward, *A Catalogue of European Scientific Instruments in the Department of Medieval and Later Antiquities of the British Museum* (London, 1981), p. 98, cat. no. 288, reg. no. 86 30, 1. Brass covered wooden rod, total length 1.392 m; signed: Nepos Gemmae Phrisy Louaný año 1571. This was Walter Arsenius.

17. Sarah Tyacke and John Huddy, *Christopher Saxton and Tudor Map-Making*, British Library Series No.2 (London, 1980), pp. 35–36; R.A. Skelton, *County Atlases of the British Isles, 1579–1703* (London, 1970), p. 7.

18. M.B. Donald, *Elizabethan Copper: The History of the Company of Mines Royal, 1568–1605* (London, 1955); M.B. Donald, *Elizabethan Monopolies: The History of the Company of Mineral and Battery Works, 1568–1604* (Edinburgh, 1961).

19. Cole's involvement is mentioned in Donald, *Monopolies*, pp. 14, 106.

20. G.L'E. Turner, 'The London Trade in Scientific Instrument-Making in the 18th Century,' *Vistas in Astronomy*, 20 (1976), 181–8; G.L'E. Turner, 'Apparatus of Science in the Eighteenth Century', *Revista da Universidade de Coimbra*, 26 (1977), 29pp.

21. For bibliographies, see F.R. Maddison, 'Early Astronomical and Mathematical Instruments. A Brief Survey of Sources and Modern Studies', *History of Science*, 2 (1963), 17–50; G.L'E. Turner, 'The History of Optical Instruments. A Brief Survey of Sources and Modern Studies', *History of Science*, 8 (1969), 53–93, reprinted and extended in G.L'E. Turner, *Essays on the History of the Microscope* (Oxford, 1980), chapter 2; G.L'E. Turner, 'Scientific Instruments', chapter 13 in *Information Sources in the History of Science and Medicine*, edited by Pietro Corsi and Paul Weindling (London, 1982).

22. E.R. Kiely, *Surveying Instruments, their History and Classroom Use* (New York, 1947); D. Chilton, 'Land Measurement in the Sixteenth Century', *Transactions of the Newcomen Society*, 31 (1957–58 & 1958–59), 111–29 (published 1961); Richeson, *Land Measuring* (note 1); Silvio A Bedini, *Thinkers and Tinkers. Early American Men of Science* (New York, 1975), which is greatly concerned with surveying; Olivia Brown, *Catalogue 1: Surveying* (Cambridge: The Whipple Museum of the History of Science, 1982); J.A. Bennett and Olivia Brown, *The Compleat Surveyor* (Cambridge: published to accompany a special exhibition at the Whipple Museum of the History of Science, 1982). Continental practice and the associated instruments have received attention from temporary exhibitions and museums: *Les Géomètres-Arpenteurs du XVIᵉ au XVIIIᵉ siècle dans nos Provinces* [exhibition for centenary of Union des Géomètres-Experts de Bruxelles, 21 May to 31 July 1976], edited by Roger Schonaerts, Introduction by Jean Mosselmans (Brussels, 1976); Herbert Wunderlich, *Kursächsische Feldmesskunst, artilleristische Richtverfahren und Ballistik im 16. und 17. Jahrhundert* [based on instruments, maps, drawings, and prints in the Staatlichen Mathematisch-Physikalischen Salons Dresden] (Berlin, 1977); Franz A Dreier, *Winkelmessinstrumente: Vom 16. bis zum frühen 19. Jahrhundert* [exhibition in Kunstgewerbemuseum 9 November 1979 to 23 February 1980] (Berlin, 1979).

    Although the studies cited above probably represent most of the writings specifically on surveying instruments, one must not neglect works on the closely related and overlapping navigational instruments. By far the most important and comprehensive of these is that by David W. Waters, *The Art of Navigation in England in Elizabethan and Early Stuart Times* (London, 1958). The instruments are of prime concern here.

23. For references, see Maddison, 'Astronomical Instruments', p. 27.

24. Maddison, 'Astronomical Instruments', p. 27. For this point, and much else relevant to the dissemination of science and technology, see the important work Elizabeth L. Eisenstein, *The Printing Press as an Agent of Change: Communications and Cultural Transformations in Early-Modern Europe*, 2 vols (Cambridge, 1979), ɪ, 139, 443.

25. R.T. Gunther, 'The Astrolabe of Queen Elizabeth', *Archaeologia*, 86 (1937), 65–72; the instrument is in the Museum of the History of Science, Oxford, Inv. no. 37–6. For a note on Greaves at Rhodes, see R.T. Gunther, *The Astrolabes of the World*, 2 vols (Oxford, 1932; reprinted in 1 vol., 1976), ɪɪ, 392.

26. Erasmus Habermel, born in Regensburg *c*1538, died Prague 1606, has a theodolite and other surveying instruments to his credit in the Museum of the History of Science, Oxford. Although 145 of his products are known, very few indeed have a

provenance further back than the middle of the nineteenth century, which is one reason why some people think not all may be genuine. For a list, see Ernst Zinner, *Deutsche und Niederländische Astronomische Instrumente des 11.–18. Jahrhunderts* (Munich, 1956), pp. 329–46. and Wolfgang Eckhardt, 'Erasmus Habermel: zur Biographie des Instrumentmachers Kaiser Rudolfs II', *Jahrbuch der Hamburger Kunstsammlungen*, 21 (1976), 55–92; 22 (1977), 13–74.

27. Joyce Brown, 'Guild organisation and the Instrument-Making Trade, 1550–1830: the Grocers' and Clockmakers' Companies', *Annals of Science*, 36 (1979), 1–34.

28. Joyce Brown, *Mathematical Instrument-Makers in the Grocers' Company, 1688–1800* (London, 1979). Note: the account begins in the sixteenth century.

29. Henri Michel, 'Gemini (Thomas Lambert ou Lambrechts, dit)', *Biographie nationale de Belgique*, 31 (1961), 386–94. It is in this article that Michel claims Humphrey Cole as a Belgian, in spite of Cole's claim to be born in England, using the argument that an Englishman would not need to say so! A more recent notice is C.D. O'Malley, 'Geminus, Thomas', *DSB*, v (1972), 347–9. Ryther also advertised his Englishness, see p. 99 above.

30. Illustrated in Henri Michel, *Scientific Instruments in Art and History*, translated by R.E.W. and F.R. Maddison (London, 1966), plate 55; the astrolabe is in the Musées royaux d'Art et d'Histoire, Brussels.

31. Richeson, *Land Measuring*, pp. 43–4, 52–3; Taylor, *Mathematical Practitioners*, pp. 23, 166–7, 317; Joy B. Easton, 'Digges, Leonard' and 'Digges, Thomas', *DSB*, IV (1971), 97–8. *Tectonicon* was printed by I. Daye for Thomas Gemini; it ran to eight editions before 1600. Both Diggeses were close friends of John Dee; French, *Dee*, pp. 98–9.

32. Bennett and Brown, *Compleat Surveyor*, pp. 4–5, and Richeson, *Land Measuring*, pp. 53–57, discuss the instruments.

33. R.T. Gunther, Preface, p.v, in a reprint of part of *Pantometria*, 'Digges Theodelitus', *Old Ashmolean Reprints IV* (Oxford, 1927).

34. The Polymetrum had no magnetic compass, otherwise it is very like Digges 'Topographical Instrument'. The well-known illustration of Waldseemüller's device first appears in the 1512 edition of Gregorius Reisch, *Margarita Philosophica* (Strasbourg). For a note on the printing history and the pirated editions, whether Freiburg or Strasbourg, see E.G.R. Taylor, 'A Regional Map of the Early XVIth Century', *Geographical Journal*, 71 (1928), 474–9 (p. 475); the map in question is Waldseemüller's.

35. R.T. Gunther, 'The Great Astrolabe and other Scientific Instruments of Humphrey Cole', *Archaeologia*, 76 (1927), 273–317 (p. 314). For Worsop, see Richeson, *Land Measuring*, pp. 74–77.

36. Cyprian Lucar, *A Treatise named Lvcarsolace Devided into Fovver Bookes* (London, 1590); the quotation from p. 10.

37. The *Dictionary of National Biography* gives Cole's dates as fl 1570–1580; Gunther, 'The Great Astrolabe', p. 315, suggests c1520–1591, the date of administration granted to the widow being 6 July 1591, and *assuming* some 70 years of life. Taylor, *Mathematical Practitioners*, p. 171, gives 1530?–1591, a more likely life span.

38. Gunther, 'The Great Astrolabe'. He lists 13 instruments signed by Cole; now 22 are known.

39. Gunther, 'The Astrolabe of Queen Elizabeth', see note 25.

40. For a listing of Cole's extant instruments, see Appendix I to this paper,

41. Brown, *Grocers' Company*, p. 58. Cole says he is a Goldsmith in the cartouche on his map of the Holy Land, illustrated in Gunther, 'The Great Astrolabe', p. 305.

42. Waters, *Art of Navigation*, pp. 200, 356–7, places this in context, and points out that Hood said he was inspired by Ramus's *Geometry* to invent the sector. There is much about Hood in Waters's book.

43. Galileo Galilei, *Operations of the Geometric and Military Compass 1606*, translated with Introduction by Stillman Drake, (Washington, D.C.: Smithsonian Institution, 1978).

44. A.M. Hind, *Engraving in England in the Sixteenth and Seventeenth Centuries*, (Cambridge, 1952), pp. 221–2.

45. Maria Luisa Righini Bonelli, *Il Museo di Storia della Scienza a Firenze* (Milan, 1968), quadrato nautico, Inv. no. 663 (plate 51), compasso altimetro, Inv. no. 2516, compasso, Inv. no. 2516 [sic], grafometro, Inv. no. 3174; pp. 164–5, 181–2. See also note 46 below.

46. John Bruce, 'Description of a pocket-Dial made in 1593 for Robert Devereux, Earl of Essex', *Archaeologia*, 40 (1866), 343–56 (p. 348).

47. The subject of the paper by Bruce was donated to the British Museum, see Ward, *Catalogue*, p. 126, cat. no. 361, reg. no. 66 2–21, 1. For Florence, see note 45 above.

48. Brown, *Grocers' Company*, p. 58.

49. See note 41 above.

50. Bonelli, *Il Museo*, p. 182, visorio o teodolite, Inv. no. 240. D.J. Bryden tells me (Sept. 1982) he has seen a second instrument signed by Ryther, a universal equinoctial dial dated 1588.

51. Illustrated in R.T. Gunther, *Early Science in Oxford*, 1 (Oxford, 1921–3; reprinted London, 1967), p. 367.

52. Brown, *Grocers' Company*, p. 24.

53. Brown, *Grocers' Company*, pp. 24–25.

54. The 1557 compendium by V.C. is fully illustrated and described in Louis Janin, 'Un compendium de poche par Humphrey Cole 1557', *Annali dell'Istituto e Museo di Storia dell Scienza di Firenze*, 1 (1976), 9–12, plus 12 pp. unnumbered. The author makes the unsubstantiated assumption that V.C. is H. Cole, an assumption not even made by Gunther (footnote 35) to whom he refers.

John Roche

The cross-staff as a surveying instrument in England 1500–1640

1. The early history of the Jacob's staff

The first version of the cross-staff, the astonomer's staff, was invented by Levi ben Gerson (1288–1344) in southern France in the early fourteenth century.[1] Levi's hand-held instrument consisted of a wooden staff about 4½ feet long, and about 1 inch wide, which was provided with six or seven perforated tablets which could slide along the staff, and which were selected according to the size of the angle to be measured. The staff was marked off into six equal divisions, the tablets being an integral multiple or fraction of a division. In use one end of the staff had to be pressed firmly near the eye, leaving the hands free to steady the staff and adjust the cross piece.[2] Levi's device was intended to fill the need for an accurate astronomical instrument which could measure directly the angular distance between stars or planets, and the diameter of the Sun and Moon. He also describes how it can be used to measure the altitudes of celestial objects.[3]

In the fifteenth century we find the first references to a very different type of cross-staff being used as a surveying instrument to measure heights, widths, and distances.[4] The earliest references to this instrument call it a Jacob's staff or a geometrical staff. The surveyor's cross-staff continued to be generally, though not always, called a Jacob's staff by practitioners until it disappeared in the late seventeenth century.[5] The Jacob's staff should not be confused with the astronomer's staff, or with the sea staff which came into use after 1514.[6] The early Jacob's staff was a simple instrument in which the cross piece was of the same length as the distance between divisions on the main staff (pl. 53). In another version a simple peg was used instead of a cross piece (pl. 54). It was very simple to use and in most applications involved pacing without calculations.

To obtain the height or width of an inaccessible tower, for example, the cross piece is set at a convenient division and the observer walks to and fro until the tower and cross piece are just seen to overlap. The cross piece is then moved one division towards the eye-end of the staff and the observer walks directly towards the tower until overlap recurs. The distance walked is then equal to the height or width of the tower. Furthermore the distance from the first station to the tower is the distance walked multiplied by the initial number of scale divisions between cross piece and eye-end of the staff.[7] Some mathematically-minded agrimensor or military engineer, perhaps, in designing the Jacob's staff, combined the mechanical and optical advantages of the astronomer's staff with the ancient technique of using crossed staves in surveying.[8] The result was an instrument which was quick and simple to use, easy and inexpensive to construct, and which could be rapidly dismantled and packed.

It was not a highly accurate instrument, however. Firstly it was supported by hand, and secondly the point of convergence of rays of light from a distant object, even were the alignment perfect, would not in general coincide with the beginning of the scale. This became known as the problem of the eccentricity of the eye. It did not matter in the measurement of heights and widths, but it did matter in the measurement of distances. It was never solved for the Jacob's staff, although it was solved for the astronomer's staff and for the sea staff.[9] Another requirement for accuracy was that the cross-piece had to be parallel to the height or width being measured. This was often difficult to achieve on the primitive form of the Jacob's staff.

Johann Werner, in a publication of 1514, was the first to put a scale in degrees on the astronomer's staff. He also showed how his instrument could be used to measure position angles between landmarks,[10] that is the angle subtended by two distant features at the eye of the observer. Position angles were being measured by German cartographers early in the sixteenth century in an attempt to get both distance and direction correct.[11] After Werner it became common, though not universal, for Jacob's staves to carry a scale in degrees as well as the usual linear scale.

In the decades following Werner's publication the astronomer's staff, the surveyor's cross-staff, and the sea staff developed rapidly, especially through the design innovations of Peter Apian and Gemma Frisius.[12] Gemma Frisius introduced sliding vanes on the cross-piece and a sliding cross-socket which could be locked into position (eg see pl. 56). The latter device meant that the cross-piece could now be adjusted so that it was accurately parallel to the object being measured.[13] Gemma Frisius used his cross-staff to attempt a longitude determination by the method of lunar distances,[14] and explained how it could be used for triangulation surveying.[15] Tycho Brahe used the same type of staff to carry out a triangulation survey in the north of Denmark during 1578–79.[16] If the field-use of an instrument can be judged from the number of publications describing it, then the sixteenth century was undoubtedly the period of greatest popularity of the surveyor's cross-staff, both of the Jacob's staff and of Gemma Frisius's version.[17]

2. Printed accounts of the surveyor's cross staff in England

I have come across no reference to a Jacob's staff in any inventory of English instruments before 1547.[18] Literary references do, however, exist. In about 1518 Nicholas Kratzer brought with him to England a manuscript describing a Jacob's staff.[19] It should be easy to establish, also, that copies of G. Reisch's *Margarita philosophica* (Friburg, 1503), P. Apian's *Cosmographicus liber* (n. 12 above), and other Latin texts containing a description of the Jacob's staff, found their way to English libraries early in the century. In 1547 John Dee (1527–1608), returned to Cambridge from Louvain with various instruments, including the 'first astronomer's staff of brass that was of Gemma Frisius's devising'.[20] It is well established that it was Dee who gave publicity to Gemma Frisius's staff as an astronomical instrument.[21] From the point of view of the literary tradition, however, he seems to have had little immediate impact on surveying practices.

The present evidence on mid-century surveying techniques in England is very scanty.[22] It would seem likely that the flurry of continental texts during the period on the uses of the cross-staff in surveying would have provoked a response in the field in England. At present no evidence clearly suggests that it did so. In 1556 Leonard Digges (1510–58) published a description of a very curious surveyor's cross-staff (pl. 55).[23] This instrument owed nothing to continental developments of the surveyor's cross staff.[24] It was a version of Werner's cross-staff with the scale in degrees replaced by the old linear scale of Levi ben Gerson. It could be fitted together in two sections giving a total length of ten feet. Such an instrument would be extremely impractical in field survey, requiring a support, two observers, and lacking a means for rendering the cross-piece parallel to the object being measured. It seems doubtful to me that such an instrument was ever constructed. It also seems to indicate a lack of field experience with the Jacob's staff by at least one gentleman surveyor, and may also indicate that the Jacob's staff was not widely used in England at that time.

The text which appears to have had the greatest impact on surveying with the cross-staff in England was Thomas Digges's *Alae seu scalae mathematicae* (London, 1573), in which a much improved version of Gemma Frisius's instrument is described. Digges explained among other things how to allow for the eccentricity of the eye. His instrument was mainly intended, however, for astronomers and navigators. The next printed account in English of the surveyor's cross-staff occurs in William Bourne's *Treasure for Travellers*, first published in 1578. Bourne describes how to determine inaccessible heights, widths, and distances, with a Gemma Frisius type of instrument.[25]

Thomas Hood's . . . *Jacob's Staff*, first published in 1590 also describes a minor modification of Gemma Frisius's instrument.[26] Thomas Blundeville, in 1597, published an account of a cross-staff for surveying which is again based on Gemma Frisius's instrument.[27] So does Arthur Hopton in *The Geodeticall Staffe* (London, 1610).[28] Edmund Gunter in *The Use of the Sector, Crosse Staffe and Other Instruments* (London, 1624) describes a continental modification of Gemma Frisius's instrument in which the cross-piece is about two thirds of the length of the main staff, instead of the more usual half length (pl. 56)[29]. There were many later editions of these works, but after 1624 I have not come across any original printed work in English on the surveyor's cross-staff, and this is surely significant.

3. The use of the Jacob's staff in field surveying in England

It is extremely difficult on present evidence to establish to what extent the cross staff was actually used in estate, cartographic, or military surveying in Elizabethan and early Stuart England. The upsurge in the number of texts on the instrument between 1578 and 1624 surely reflects an increased use of it. The mathematical arts in general were cultivated more energetically during that period.[30] This apparent interest in the instrument, however, is not very evident in the more technical texts written for professional surveyors. The works of Richard Benese (1537)[31], Valentine Leigh (1577)[32], Edward Worsop (1582)[33], Cyprian Lucar (1590)[34], Ralph Agas (1596)[35], John Norden (1607)[36], Aaron Rathborne (1616)[37], and William Leybourne (1653)[38], hardly allude to the cross-staff. Rathborne, in his standard text, *The Surveyor* (1616) states that 'the instruments now most in use are the Theodelite, Plaine-table, and Circumferentor'.[39]

There are some scraps of evidence concerning the use of the surveyor's cross-staff, however. The frontispiece of the 1579 edition of the Christopher Saxton's atlas of

England and Wales contains an illustration of a cross-staff. The instrument depicted is a sea staff, however, and cannot be regarded as reliable evidence that Saxton actually used the instrument in his surveys. Thomas Hood provides more reliable evidence. One of his interlocutors refers to having 'seen men . . . who, measuring the height of a thing, have made no matter how they held their staffe'.[40] Sir William Lower, writing from Wales in 1607 to Thomas Harriot speaks of a cross- staff (of the Gemma Frisius type) which he used for the measuring of lands.[41] John Greaves, geometry professor at Gresham College, London, in about 1640 used a cross-staff of Thomas Digges's design to measure the base and height of the 'first and fairest pyramid' at Memphis.[42]

Cross-staves, therefore, were being used for surveying in England in the late sixteenth and early seventeenth century. The extent of their use is more difficult to establish. During the same period far more accurate instruments were coming into use among surveyors. I would hazard a guess that surveyors usually carried cross-staves on their surveys, and that these were used to make quick trial estimates in preparation for more accurate measurements. Saxton may have used a cross-staff in this manner. Further light on this question will come from the manuscript evidence. It would be most helpful if military, cartographic, and local historians of the period could include a mention in their publications of any manuscript references to the surveyor's cross-staff.

1. B.R. Goldstein, *The Astronomical Tables of Levi Ben Gerson* (New Haven, Conn, 1974), 19–20; J. Roche, 'The Radius Astronomicus in England', *Annals of Science*, 38 (1981), 1–9.

2. Roche, p. 5–7; B. Goldstein, 'Levi Ben Gerson: instrumental errors and the transversal scale', *Journal for the History of Astonomy*, 8 (1977), 102–112.

3. Roche, p. 5: references to primary sources are provided.

4. Theodor Ruffi, 'Ad conficiendum baculum geometrium alias baculum Jacob . . .', Bayerische Staatsbibliothek Munich, Latin codex 11067 (*c*1445–50), f. 207v.

5. *eg* T. Hood, *The Use of Two Mathematicall Instruments, the Crosse Staffe . . . and the Jacob's Staffe* (London, 1590); see also Roche, pp. 3, 9–10.

6. L. de Albuquerque, 'Astronomical navigation', in A. Cortesão (ed.) *A History of Portuguese Cartography*, 2 vols (Coimbra, 1971), II, 365.

7. (a) E. Gunter, *The Description and Use of the Sector, the Crosse-Staffe and other instruments* (facsimile ed., Amsterdam and New York 1971; 1st ed., London, 1623), 4–8;
   (b) E.R. Kiely, *Surveying Instruments: their History and Classroom Use* (New York, 1947), 312–14, 318–19, 333–37;
   (c) L. de Albuquerque, 'Instrumentos, abacos e graficos na nauticá portugesa dos sécules XVI e XVIII', *Vertice*, 26 (1966), 706–28, (pp. 713–15).

8. Kiely, p. 14, pp. 37–39, pp. 62–63.

9. T. Digges, *Alae seu scalae mathematicae* (London, 1573), sigs 1r and 1v and 2r; J. Davis, *The Seaman's Secrets* (London, 1643; 1st ed., 1595), p. 29; Roche, pp. 5–6, pp. 22–23.

10. J. Werner, *Nova translatio primi libri cl. Ptolomaei* (Nuremberg, 1614), sigs d1r–e1v

11. E.G.R. Taylor, 'A regional map of the early XVIth Century', *Geographical Journal*, 71 (1928), 474–479.

12. P. Apian, *Cosmographicus liber* (Weyssenburg, 1524), ff.30r–32r; *Instrument Buch* (Ingolstadt, 1533), sigs n1r–n4r; Gemma Frisius, *De radio astronomico* (Antwerp, 1545); Gemma Frision, *Le ray astronomique* (transl. J. Bellère, Antwerp, 1581).

13. Gemma Frision, pp. 264–265.

14. Gemma Frisius, ff. 38r–41r.

15. Gemma Frisius, ff.21r–24v.

16. N.D. Haasbroek, *Gemma Frisius, Tycho Brahe, and Snellius and their Triangulations* (Delft, 1968), 7, 16–58.

17. Roche, footnotes 63, 113.

18. J.D. North, *Richard of Wallingford*, 3 vols (Oxford, 1976), iii, appendix 2, and appendix 15.

19. J.D. North, 'Nicholas Kratzer: the King's Astronomer', in *Science and History: studies in honour of Edward Rosen*; Studia Copernicana XVI (Warsaw, Krakow, Gdansk, 1978), 205–234, (p. 223).

20. *Autobiographical Tracts of Dr. John Dee*, edited by J. Crossley, Chetham Society, XXIV (Manchester, 1851), p. 5.

21. Dee, P. 6; J. Roche, pp. 18–23.

22. Kiely, pp. 103–107; A.W. Richeson, *English Land Measuring to 1800: instruments and practices* (Cambridge, Mass, and London, 1960), pp. 29–42; S. Tyacke and J. Huddy, *Christopher Saxton and Tudor map-making* (London, 1980), pp. 19–23.

23. L. Digges, *Tectonicon* (London, 1556), sigs Fi r.–F iv v.

24. Richeson is mistaken on this point, p. 56.

25. W. Bourne, *The Treasure for Travellers* (London, 1578), pp. 17–25.

26. T. Hood, *The use of the two Mathematicall Instruments, the Crosse Staffe . . . and the Jacob's Staffe* (Amsterdam, 1972; facsimile of the 1596 edition, London).

27. T. Blundeville, *His Exercises . . .* (London, 1597), ff. 325r–339r.

28. Hood, pp. 95–98.

29. Roche, pp. 25–31.

30. E.G.R. Taylor, *The Mathematical Practitioners of Tudor and Stuart England 1485–1714* (Cambridge, 1954), pp. 323-345.

31. R. de Benese, . . . *The maner of measurynge all maner of lande* (Southwarke, 1537?).

32. V. Leigh, *The most Profitable and Commendable Science of Surveying of Landes* (London, 1562).

33. E. Worsop, *Sundrie Errours and Faults Daily Committed by Land-meaters* (London, 1582).

34. C. Lucar, *A Treatise named Lucarsolace* (London, 1590).

35. R. Agas, *A Preparative to Plotting of Landes and Tenements for Surveying* (London, 1596).

36. J. Norden, *The Surveyor's Dialogue* (London, 1607).

37. A. Rathborne, *The Surveyor* (London, 1616).

38. W. Leybourn, *The Compleat Surveyor* (London, 1653).

39. Rathborne, p. 123. He does, however, mention Hopton's 'geodeticall staffe'.

40. T. Hood (facsimile of 1596 edition), sig. Cii verso.

41. Petworth House HMC 241/vii, f.2.

42. *Miscellaneous Works of Mr. John Greaves*, edited by T. Birch, 2 vols (London, 1737), i, 92–93; Bodley MS Savile 49(1), ff.44v.–45r.

William Ravenhill

Christopher Saxton's surveying: an enigma

No consensus exists among historians of cartography, in spite of a number of recent pronouncements by them, about the surveying techniques used by Christopher Saxton. He himself is singularly silent on the subject. The known supporting documents have been searched for clues but until others come to light, his maps alone remain. The delayed decoding of what lies behind the making of these artefacts could be due to their not being examined collectively, and, in particular, the two great masterpieces, the so-called *Atlas* containing the small general map, *Anglia*, with the thirty-four county maps and Britannia Insularum . . . , the large general map of 1583. It is time to examine all of these as the outcome of a single integrated mapping operation. Furthermore, the undoubted quality and sophistication of the large map has not been sufficiently explored and explained, either in terms of the field survey which was necessary for its compilation or in the high measure of control which it exhibits. Although no specific and personal information appears to survive, genera-tions of surveyors have faced the same challenge – a vast landscape to be put on paper. Is not retrospection into the contexts of both space and time a feasible way forward? A more field-oriented approach is therefore advocated, in conjuction with an appreciation of the contemporary state of local and national affairs.

This particular surveying enigma has not lacked inquisitors, and, over the last fifty-five years, verdicts have oscillated between some form of triangulation and that of traversing. The modern period of enquiry can usefully begin with Edward Heawood, who in 1926, implicitly prefers triangulation[1] and one year later R.T. Gunther comes down firmly in favour of triangulation, tracing its diffusion to Britain from the Dutch cartographer Gemma Frisius.[2] Sir George Fordham, in his pioneering monograph, published in 1928, entitled *Christopher Saxton of Dunningley*[3] speaks eloquently of 'Saxton's technical skill as a surveyor, and of his capacity as a draughtsman' but 'of the instruments and methods he made use of in the field we know nothing.' A categorical statement by E.G.R. Taylor on this problem has not been found but she was certain that both instruments and techniques for triangulation were at Saxton's disposal.[4] In the middle 1930s the view that triangulation was the method employed by him was to the fore.

The case for traversing gained adherents after the publication of Professor Manley's paper 'Saxton's Survey of Northern England' in 1934.[5] G.R. Crone was not convinced when he wrote *Maps and their Makers* in 1953[6] but P.D.A. Harvey and Harry Thorpe in 1959 followed Manley's lead.[7] R.A. Skelton, in his monograph on the large general map,[8] not in its final form when he died in 1970, did not come to a firm view. He stated that Saxton 'proceeded by traverse lines'; and then agrees with Manley about Saxton 'viewing from a few hill tops'; he may have used the plane table; 'it is improbable he employed any form of triangulation'; but note his telling remark 'the controls of his mapping must have been supplied by rays between distant points of intervisibility' and by 'determinations of latitude'. Ifor M. Evans and Heather Lawrence[9] conclude that the issue 'remains a matter for reasoned speculation' while P.D.A. Harvey[10] holds the view that 'Saxton's maps of the English and Welsh Counties in the 1570s were probably simply itinerary maps made without triangulation.' Recently, Sarah Tyacke and John Huddy,[11] in their volume to accompany the exhibition at the British Library of Tudor Mapping, incline towards the use of a form of triangulation. More recently, A.H.W. Robinson[12] concludes, by way of an analysis of the Leicestershire map, 'that Saxton did not make use of a road traverse or triangulation framework.' There are always dangers in quoting out of context and in summarising, but, allowing for this, it is my hope that the above references give a fair coverage of views to date without gross misrepresentation. To sum up, one thing is certain: our collective uncertainty.

Of the views expressed, the majority refer to, or indeed quote, Manley, and many agree with him. It is important, however, to interpret him correctly. Manley is using the term *traverse* loosely, and not in the way in which modern surveying texts and surveyors employ it. He is discussing not open traverses using polar co-ordinates, but radiation from a station by bearing and estimate. What is more, he is considering the insertion of details on the maps of a few counties in the north of England. Within the context in which he was writing, what he discovered was most important, but his article does not attempt any analysis of the large general map, or investigate the question of control. With regard to traversing (the open kind) polar co-ordinates along roads, itineraries, I still do not think that this kind of data was available in the sixteenth century or the early years of the seventeenth century.[13] Moreover, open traverses do not provide a control unless their terminal points are fixed by other means. Had all this information about roads been collected in the course of Saxton's survey, there is little doubt that he would have placed them on the maps, such was their economic, social, and strategic importance. Even the Fosse Way, requiring but a straight line across several county maps, has not been inserted.

An examination of the large general map reveals a number of highly sophisticated features. The use of the Donis projection, the placing of the graticule, the choice of the central meridian and its relationship to a prime meridian passing through the Azores – all these point to continental antecedents and, in particular, to Gerard Mercator. Unlike the *Atlas*, which is county and regional in flavour, the general map is national, even global. In another place, an attempt has been made to associate these global aspects with John Dee,[14] but exciting as the use of geographical co-ordinates may be and good as the latitudes in particular are, it is difficult to be persuaded that they provided the control for this map. In this period, just as they were many decades later, graticules were doubtlessly superimposed on drawn maps so that appropriate co-ordinate intersections could be made to coincide with one or two places whose geographical positions had been ascertained by astronomical methods. The inspiration for the control features of the large map must again be sought in continental sources, and who is more likely as the agent of this diffusion than John Dee? After Robert Recorde's death in 1558, John Dee became the most influential teacher and adviser on scientific subjects in England, and he retained this position for the next quarter of a century. He had formed close relationships with Gerard Mercator and Gemma Frisius. The influence of the former has been detected in the projection; the genius of the latter is seen in his *Libellus de locorum describendorum ratione*, first published in 1533, a copy of which graced the shelves of John Dee's library at Mortlake.[15]

It was Gemma Frisius who appreciated that the astrolabe, which acquired its position by gravity in the vertical plane, as an altitude-measuring device, could also function similarly in azimuth when levelled horizontally. The *Libellus* goes on to explain and illustrate how a third point in the landscape can be fixed from two known points by intersecting rays. The other requirement for this early form of triangulation is the known length of one side of a triangle. This was obtained either by direct measurement or by the use of a system of right-angled similar triangles.[16] The *Libellus* therefore, offers a complete treatise on triangulation, and is an important landmark in the history of cartography. John Dee would have become familiar at first hand with this new technique during his residence at Louvain during the period 1546–1548.

In addition to techniques, successful surveying also required appropriate and good instruments. These were also to hand in Britain, and were again based on antecedents and skills of continental origin. In the sixteenth century Flemish engravers came to London to escape religious persecution, and so provided the nucleus of a scientific instrument-making trade. Thomas Gemini (fl 1524–1562) was a leader in these skills, and he was followed by Humphrey Cole (1520–1591), the first of our English mathematical-instrument makers.[17]

The involvment of the Crown and Government in map-making has been explored, and due emphasis has been given to the organisational and administrative purposes which map-making was destined to serve.[18] In so doing, have scholars made much of this issue to the exclusion of one more telling? For example, it has been claimed that the consistent appearance of those paled parks on county maps is to do with the pride and prestige of the emerging Elizabethan gentry. No doubt there is much truth in that. Equally, if not more, significant, may be the fact that from 1536, the twenty-seventh year of Henry VIII's reign, the government was deeply concerned that 'the brede of horses is sore decayed' and all the owners of parks of up to two miles in circumference had to keep two breeding mares and four mares in parks over that size.[19] This statutory obligation was still in force everywhere in the realm in 1569, a year when a return was demanded.[20] This reflected the growing tension in relations between Spain and England. In this same context, has the possibility been overlooked that Saxton's mapping was part of the military preparedness? Elizabeth's reign was one requiring continuous vigilance, and in the late 1560s the situation at home and abroad was becoming more threatening and dangerous. In subsequent history such times have frequently been those most conducive to investment in and production of maps. Speed was of the essence. The techniques, the instruments, the input from the cognoscenti at home and abroad, government support and indirect finance, the right man for the job – all these set a perfect stage, but for one omission. How to do the actual mapping consistently county after county? In five summer seasons? Less than one month for each county? A vital feature of the Elizabethan context has been overlooked. Who could have been relied upon to provide Saxton, a stranger, with the landscape data required in every county of the realm?

In 1567 the build-up of a strong Spanish army in the Netherlands constituted a real threat, and was so understood by Elizabeth and her Privy Council. As the political situation deteriorated the musters, which had formerly been called every three years, were now more frequent. On 26 March 1569 the Privy Council issued a directive to all counties to hold a general muster of all able-bodied men over the age of sixteen.[21] Christopher Saxton would have been an active twenty-five- or twenty-seven-year-old. With the musters went the beacon system. Note the phrase, as the whole is more than the sum of the parts. It constituted a nationwide, well-organised, intervisibly-linked communication system, which was centuries old by 1569: orders about it appear in the State Papers at intervals from 1324;[22] these orders become more numerous in Elizabeth's reign.[23] They reveal a comprehensive system, one being brought to a high state of readiness in the early 1570s and one regarded as an important part of the defence of the realm. Those responsible gave the system great thought so as to bring it to perfection. There was, for example, a chain of command from the Crown to county level, through Lords Lieutenant to Deputy Lieutenants to Justices of the Peace to High Constables of the Hundreds and Petty Constables of the Parishes.[24]

Christopher Saxton, therefore, need not have arrived cartographically empty handed in an unfamiliar landscape of a county. There was a maintained, manned set of known intervisible viewpoints, the system incorporating over-lapping connections between the counties of the realm.

The word *beacon*, (of Teutonic origin) is first introduced into the Latin of an ordinance in 1372, where it appears in the form 'common signals by fire (*signum per ignem*) on hills and high places called Beknes',[25] and the repetition of the phrase in the letter of the Privy Council to the Justices and other officers in Wales, 10 July 1576 should not pass unnoticed.

An open L^{ett}re to all Justic^{e}s of peace mayo^{u}rs & oth^{e}rs etc w^{i}thin the severall Shieres of Wales. That where the bearer hereof ^{Christ}ofer Saxton is appointed by her Ma^{ies}tie vnder her signe and signet to set forth and describe in Coat^{e}s p^{ar}ticulerlie all the shieres in Wales. That the said Justic^{e}s shalbe aiding and assisting vnto him to see him conducted vnto any towre Castle highe place or hill to view that countrey, and that he may be accompanied w^{i}th ij or iij honest men such as do best know the cuntrey for the better accomplishment of that service, and that at his departure from any towne or place that he hath taken the view of the said towne do set forth a horseman that can speke both welshe and englishe to safe conduct him to the next market Towne, etc[26]

The message being relayed in this letter is vital, in so far as it provides the only direct evidence so far found which gives unequivocal insights into the methods of survey used by, and the local support available to, Saxton. It will be reasonable to assume that what applied to Wales would be equally applicable to the counties of England. The specific mention of 'towre Castle highe place or hill' is consistent with the use of triangulation, and the Justices of the Peace are instructed not only to see Saxton conducted to such high viewpoints but also to ensure that he was accompanied by two or three honest men who knew the landscape. Although the word 'beacon' does not specifically occur in this letter, the whole tenor of the message is entirely consistent with the known organisation of the beacon system. In the first place it was under the jurisdiction of the Justices of the Peace; furthermore the watch was normally to be kept by two or three trustworthy men, as the following extract from a long entry in the State Papers of 1560 makes clear:

Orders taken at Wynchester by Lord St. John and the reste of the Justices of the Peace in the Countie of South^t the xiii^th Daye of Maye Anno Regine Elizabeth Secundo . . .

Item, yt is further agreed that the beacons shall be presently furnished with wood sufficient readye to be fyered upon any occasyon and wood layed by for mayneteynenge the fyer and that the said beacons shalbe presentlie watched viz. in the daye tyme with two honeste and substanciall p'sones and in the nyght with three at the least, and they shall not be fyered at any time with-oute the consent of some justyce of peace . . .[27]

The other important point made in the 'open Lettre' – the provision of men who 'best know the cuntrey' – can also be accommodated in the contemporary orders for the beacons. Those who watched, besides being 'wise and vigilant' had to be men of 'understanding' who were able to recognise precisely their nearest-neighbour beacons, that is 'the watchers on the hills both on the coast and inland, taking heed not to be deceived by other fires'; and again, the watchers 'must take hede that they fier not ther beakons unadvisedlie uppon any other fyers whatsoever shall fortune, in any place then uppon the view'.[28] A beacon alarm had to be differentiated from other bonfires. There had been genuine errors of identification as well as cases of vandalism, hoaxes and the activities of *agents provocateurs*. Four such incidents before, during and after the period of Saxton's mapping endorse the point being made. In 1545 'the King's subjects of the county of Worcester, upon a second firing of the beacons of Oxfordshire, set forward towards Portismowthe, and after three days' journey received, between Wantage and Newbery, about 10 am, the Council's letters for their retirement until again warned'.[29] In the same month Sussex passed a false alarm to Kent, whereupon Sir Richard Long, who led the Kentish forces, sent a most indignant report to London.[30] On two occasions, in 1560 and 1579, the beacon on Portsdown was unnecessarily fired, the second incident arising when the watchers were deceived by hunters trying to smoke a badger out of his earth.[31] By 1586 such incidents brought a swift and stern reaction from the Privy Council, as 'A letter to the Sheriffe and Justices of the Peace in the countie of Somerset' makes clear:

Wheras of late uppon a casuall fier happening about the cittie of Bathe the countrie was like to have risen, (the watches of the Beacons neere there-abouts supposing the same to have been a Becon fired), they are required to give speciall charge to such as are and shall be appointed to the ordinarie watches of the Beacons in that Countie generallie to make speciall observance and marke of the Beacons standing upon the coastes of the contrie that if anie casuall fiers should happen hereafter in anie place thereabout within their view, they maie be able to distinguish and discerne the same from the Becons, that they be not deceaved and uppon needles occasion move the contrie to rise as aforesaid; wherof they are required that speciall care may be had and to certifie what they shall have don.[32]

What is made clear by these references is that the watchers at a particular beacon would have been able to direct Saxton's theodolite open sights to a round of known places and to the neighbouring beacons, the system thus providing a logic to a landscape which would otherwise be strange, bewildering and unknown. Further-more, he could rely on the system being in operation and available to him everywhere in the realm in the summer months. This brings out the absolutely vital importance of his being in possession of the 'placart' or pass issued to an individual by the government or one of its agents. Such a pass was issued to Saxton on 11 March 1576. The problems arising from not having one, or, having had one, not having had it subsequently ratified, are conspicuously exemplified in the case of the other notable

Elizabethan surveyor, John Norden, the non-renewal of whose pass led to the abandonment of his *Speculum Britanniae*.[33]

The point has already been made about the nationwide coverage, whereby all counties, those on the coast as well as those inland, formed part of the intricate web of the system. To explore, therefore, how the system could have been used by Saxton, discussion can be confined to one or two counties. Devon, with two coastal and two land boundaries, with a varied topography and an area which ranks it the third largest county in England and Wales, is a good example. The enquiry as to how Saxton proceeded can usefully be set into a spatial-analysis context, in so far as one seeks to derive a workable arrangement of 'service' points. If a theoretical landscape of the Christallerian-isotropic-plain type is assumed, what particular arrangement of instrument stations (service points) will provide a minimum number to cover the whole area of Devon? If beacons are assumed as placed to provide a twelve-to fourteen- mile panoramic view and visibility to plot the direction of the nearest-neighbour beacons with the distances to them, guessed as Manley suggested, then the minimum number of beacons required to provide coverage for such an isotropic Devon is expressed by the lattice of seven or eight hexagons in pl. 57. With a scale-change to allow no more than twelve to fourteen miles between beacons, so envisaging a round of angles well within the capacity of open-sight instruments, the number of stations again expressed by the hexagonal map, pl. 58, rises to twenty-three or twenty-four.

This exercise is useful in providing some idea of the order of magnitude required for the beacon system in Devon. The transition from a purely theoretical to an actual landscape has been facilitated in the case of Devon by the work done by one of the county's local historians, Percy Russell.[34] His researches led him to conclude that there were eighty-eight Elizabethan beacons, to which more recent research has added a further three. The distribution of all these beacons is shown on pl. 59; differentiated are thirty-four whose existence before and during Elizabeth's reign has been authenticated. This is not to say that the others did not exist, but all sources are not provided by Russell, and the existence of more beacons will almost certainly be proved as more Church-wardens' accounts are studied. Sufficient are known, however, to add credibility to the argument that the beacon system in Devon could have provided Saxton with the means to prosecute a survey using triangulation.

When Cornwall is subjected to a similar treatment the hexagon lattice (pl. 60) reveals that some twelve to fourteen 'service points' would command an isotropic Cornwall. This far in the search eighteen pre-1600 beacons have been authenticated in various records with a further sixteen appearing by 1700. As in Devon, so in Cornwall, these figures indicate a part only of the total number of beacons which must have existed. John Norden, who paid particular attention to Cornwall for his projected *Speculum Britanniae*, stated that, 'Everye parish in Cornwall, for the moste parte, hath a beacon'.[35] This may be interpreted as meaning not that every parish had a beacon within its boundary but that every parish had one visible. It is inconceivable that there was one for each of the parishes named by Norden. He does, however, differentiate the status of beacons, giving pride of place to Haynboro (Hensbarrow 313m).

wheron standeth the principall beacon in Cornwall as in a place beste deseruing it; for vpon that hill a man bendinge his eye to whatsoeuer parte, shall obserue that all the Countrye rounde about it as it were falleth at the feete of this. And from this hill maybe be seene a parte of *Deuon-shire* eastewarde aboue 30 myles, and almoste to the landes ende westewarde aboue 40 myles: The seas north and south, with there dispersed Iles, are likewise playnlye discouered.[36]

Whatever 'number of Elizabethan beacons further search may produce enough are known to lend support to the view that they could have formed the instrument stations for a triangulation survey developed on a measured base-line or on several base-lines. Much more likely is the latter and almost certain is it that the field-work was carried out on a county schedule. The modern principle of making a map by working from the whole to the part does not fit the Elizabethan surveying scene, and independent surveys of individual counties subsequently joined together would more likely have been the scheme adopted. A particularly good example of such a piecing together leading Saxton into error exists in the junction of Cornwall to Devon where the former's orientation is many degrees from reality. His arrangement of triangles would also not necessarily have resembled the ordered network of well-conditioned triangles with which surveyors nowadays are familiar. The preliminary reconnaissances required to bring such order and form are difficult to accommodate within the time which Saxton actually took to complete the work. Much more feasible would appear to be the use of the resection technique, whereby the plotting of a station occupied can be effected; the field data required are: two visible stations, their positions already established, and a ray from one of them to the station occupied. This, plus the more usual establishment of stations by intersection of rays, would have allowed Saxton to progress through the landscape. One must envisage him taking a comprehensive round of rays to all points of topographic detail, together with the beacons within view and all these angles booked relative to a reference object. An equally comprehensive plotting of the data from his survey books during the progress of the field work would have ensured a smooth and orderly sequence to the project.

1. Edward Heawood, 'Some Early County Maps', *Geographical Journal*, 68 (1926), p. 325.

2. R.T. Gunther, 'The Astrolabe; its uses and derivatives', *Scottish Geographical Magazine*, 43 (1927), 135–47.

3. Sir George Fordham, 'Christopher Saxton of Dunningley his life and work', Thoresby Society's *Miscellanea*, 28 (Leeds, 1928), pp. 356–84 and 491.

4. E.G.R. Taylor, 'The Earliest Account of Triangulation', *Scottish Geographical Magazine*, 43 (1927), 341–5.

5. Gordon Manley, 'Saxton's Survey of Northern England', *Geographical Journal*, 83 (1934), 308–16.

6. G.R. Crone, *Maps and their Makers* (London, 1953), p. 108.

7. P.D.A. Harvey and Harry Thorpe, *The Printed Maps of Warwickshire 1576–1900* (Warwick, 1959), p. 2.

8. R.A. Skelton, *Saxton's Survey of England and Wales* Imago Mundi Supplement, No. VI (Amsterdam, 1974), p. 9.

9. Ifor M. Evans and Heather Lawrence, *Christopher Saxton Elizabethan Map-Maker* (Wakefield, 1979), p. 44.

10. P.D.A. Harvey, *The History of Topographical Maps* (London, 1980), p. 163.

11. Sarah Tyacke and John Huddy, *Christopher Saxton and Tudor map-making* (London, 1980), p. 32.

12. A.H.W. Robinson, 'Christopher Saxton and the mapping of the Leicestershire landscape' in *Leicestershire Geographical Essays* Occasional Publication No. 1 (1980), 67–75.

13. William Ravenhill, *John Norden's Manuscript Maps of Cornwall and its Nine Hundreds* (Exeter, 1972), pp. 26–7; John Norden, *Intended Guyde for English Travailers* (London, 1625).

14. William Ravenhill, 'Projections for the Large General Maps of Britain', *Imago Mundi*, 33 (1981), 21–32.

15. Gemma Frisius, *Libellus de locorum describendorum ratione* annexed to Petrus Apianus, *Cosmographia Liber* (Antwerp, 1533).
   E.G.R. Taylor, *Tudor Geography 1485–1583* (London, 1930) Contemporary Libraries, Appendix II, p. 196.

16. A. Pogo, 'Gemma Phrysius, his Method of Determining Differences of Longitude by Transporting Timepieces (1530), and his Treatise on Triangulation (1533)', *Isis*, 22 (1934–5), 469–85.

17. R.T. Gunther, 'The Great Astrolabe and other Scientific Instruments of Humphrey Cole', *Archaeologia*, 76 (1927), 273–317. See above pp. 98–9.

18. R.A. Skelton, *Saxton's Survey of England and Wales*, p. 8.

19. *The Statutes at Large*, IV edited by Danby Pickering. (Cambridge, 1763), pp. 353–4.

20. *The Devon Muster Roll for 1569*, edited by A.J. Howard and T.L. Stoate. (Bristol, 1977), p. iv.

21. Howard and Stoate, p. iii, quoting PRO SP 12/49 and SP 12/61.

22. H.T. White, 'The Beacon System in Hampshire', *Hampshire Field Club Archaeological Society Papers and Proceedings*, 10 (1931), 252–78, quotes the following documentary references to beacons:
   Caxton, *Cronycles of the Londe of Englod* (1480).
   Cal. Inq. Misc. File 99, m.10.
   Close Rolls 46 Ed. III May 14.
   Rymer, 7 Ed. IV, 8 Ed. IV, 3 Henry VI.
   H.T. White, 'The Beacon System in Kent', *Archaeologia Cantiana*, 46 (1934), 77–96, quotes the following:
   Rymer, 20 Ed. II, Aug. 10.
   Close Rolls 12 Ed. III, Aug. 15.
   Lambeth MS 709.

See also *Letters and Papers of Henry VIII*, edited by James Gairdner, (1883) p. 177. *Letters and Papers of Henry VIII*, 14, Part 1 (1894) p. 209; 19, Part 2 (1905) p. 279; 20, Part 1 (1905) pp. 24, 279, 345, 469, 505, 573, 622.

23. *Calendar of State Papers, Domestic Series of the Reigns of Edward VI, Mary, Elizabeth 1547–1580*, edited by Robert Lemon, (London, 1856) pp. 100 and 471.
   Ethel Lega Weekes, 'County Armaments in Devon in the Sixteenth Century', *Transactions of the Devonshire Association.*, 41 (1909), p. 355.
   Sir Henry Ellis, 'On the Early History of the Lords Lieutenants of Counties', *Archaeologia*, 35 (London, 1853), pp. 350–8, quoting Lansdowne MS 155, f. 297b, 299, 303.
   Lambeth MS 247, Part 1, f. 3, quoted in H.T. White, unpublished MS Devon Record Office 56/16.
   Acts of the Privy Council New Series, edited by John Roche Dasent, 11 (London, 1895), pp. 271, 288, 311, 350.

24. Lindsay Boynton, *The English Militia 1558–1638* (London, 1967), pp. 16 and 137.
   G. Scott Thomson 'The Origin and Growth of the Office of Deputy Lieutenant', *Transactions of the Royal Historical Society*, 4th Series, 5 (1922), 150–66.
   Lambeth MS 247, f. 3, see note 23.

25. Close Rolls, 46 Ed. III May 14, quoted in H.T. White, 'The Beacon System in Hampshire', p. 257.

26. PRO Privy Council Register, 2.11, transcribed by Alison Quinn. See R.A. Skelton, *Saxton's Survey of England and Wales*, p. 16.

27. *CSP* May 1560, SP 12, quoted in H.T. White, 'The Beacon System in Hampshire', p. 263.

28. *Letters and Papers of Henry VIII*, 20, part 1 (1905), p. 24, sub. 12 Jan. 1545.
   Lambeth MS 709, Quoted in H.T. White, 'The Beacon System in Kent', p. 83, referring to the year 1546.

29. *Letters and Papers of Henry VIII*, 20, part 1, (1905), p. 653.

30. *Letters and Papers of Henry VIII*, 20, part 1; p. 642.

31. *Acts of the Privy Council New Series*, 11 (London, 1895), p. 354.
   Lindsay Boynton, p. 137, quoting PRO SP 12/12/48–9.

32. *Acts of the Privy Council New Series*, 14, (London, 1897) pp. 93–4.

33. Ravenhill, *Norden's Maps of Cornwall*, pp. 15–20.

34. Percy Russell, 'Fire Beacons in Devon', *Transactions of the Devonshire Association*, 87 (1955), 250–302.

35. BL Harleian MS 6252 f. 39v.

36. BL Harleian MS 6252 f. 45v.

Index